THE SEBASTIAN MINIATURES COLLECTORS GUIDE

Prescott W. Baston

THE
SEBASTIAN MINIATURES
COLLECTORS GUIDE

COMPILED WITH COMMENTARIES
BY DR. GLENN S. JOHNSON

Copyright © 1980 by Sebastian Studios
Library of Congress catalog card number: 80-50276

Published in Worcester, Massachusetts, by Commonwealth Press
All rights reserved by Sebastian Miniatures
Printed in the United States of America

ABOUT THIS GUIDE

I have been involved with Prescott Baston and his Sebastian Miniatures for a little over four years.

In 1976, when Mr. Baston started closing down operations in his 30-year-old studio in Marblehead, collector letters and telephone calls began coming in to Lance's distribution center. We tried to answer all the questions. "When did you make such-and-such?" "I have a miniature that looks like so-and-so. What is it and how many did you make?" And so on.

As the number of dealers and collectors grew, especially since national distribution in July, 1978, the number of inquiries increased. It became obvious that a collector's guide was needed, and quickly.

Mr. Baston and I prepared a stopgap instrument, "The Sebastian Story and Chronology." Based on easily available copyright papers, Mr. Baston came up with a listing of 283 miniatures issued since 1938. 230 were listed as designed for retail sales and the remaining 53 as private commission pieces.

As with all hastily-prepared stopgaps, the "Chronology" lacked accuracy and completeness. Collectors wrote to tell us they had a "George and Martha Washington" dated 1938 instead of the listed 1939. They wrote to tell us they had a "Doctor" mounted on a large pedestal. It became obvious that we had listed many incorrect dates and also that we had overlooked many miniatures.

We received letters describing the features of a miniature that we could not identify. When asked, Mr. Baston would respond: "Oh yes, that would be the 'Scotch Lass' I did for Jello." Also, collectors wanted to know how many "Doc Berrys" were made. "About 150," Mr. Baston replied. "I designed the figurine for Doc Berry's birthday to help him raise money for his boys' camp."

Three conclusions were obvious:

1. A growing number of collectors wanted growing amounts of information on their collection.
2. The only complete source of this information was in copyright files, Mr. Baston's memory, the myriad of miniatures stored in the old Marblehead Studio and in Mr. Baston's trust.
3. A plan was needed urgently to bring the demand and supply together.

I had spent hundreds of hours over the years with Mr. Baston; at the studio, at collector shows, at store public appearances, at dining rooms in hotels far away from Massachusetts. As I talked to him and his collectors, Mr. Baston, his work and the collection took shape in my mind. In July, 1979, we were ready to move.

Mr. Baston, his wife and son gathered all the miniatures and copyright details. This took three months. In November, we concentrated three days on final assembly of the collection. Starting with the "Shaker Man" (1938) on the upper left hand corner and ending with "Snow Days—Boy" (1979) seven long shelves down, the 411 miniatures were placed in chronological order. Slips of paper were placed on the shelves where the copyright papers indicated the existence of a miniature that could not be located. Some miniatures existed only as white castings. We decided not to paint them. With the miniatures, the castings and notes in place, the physical "outline" was ready.

In November, we set three days aside for dictation and photography. I handed Mr. Baston a miniature, he studied it for a moment, and then told us the story behind the miniature. Mrs. Emma Abt typed as he spoke. When we had completed dictation on four or five miniatures, I took them to another room where Albert Miller photographed them.

Mr. Baston displayed an uncanny memory for names and places. His obvious love of literature was reflected in his glowing accounts of his many Dickens, Shakespeare, Mark Twain, Washington Irving and Nathaniel Hawthorne figurines. His obvious love of American history was reflected in his prideful accounts of famous persons, from the Menotomy Indian to Christopher Columbus, from Henry Hudson to Abraham Lincoln, from Johnny Appleseed to John F. Kennedy.

His obvious love of his native New England was reflected in the recited minutiae of Salem's House of Seven Gables, Plymouth's Pioneer Village and Boston's Public Gardens. All of these, and more, unfolded as the man literally shared with us his life, his work and his deepest convictions.

With only a few breaks, the task was completed in three days. Then my task began. I studied the photos and texts for completeness and detail. An SML (Sebastian Miniature Listing) number was assigned to each miniature. The photos were coupled to the copy. Then I submitted all the work to Commonwealth Press, Worcester, Massachusetts.

Mrs. Judy Wilson, Acting Director of the Sebastian Miniatures Collectors Society, and I proofread printer's galleys. The work stands as published.

I wish to acknowledge the assistance of:

Mrs. Emma Abt; interpretation and typing above and beyond the call of duty.

Mr. Albert Miller; photographing three-dimensional objects to appear on flat paper with professional skill and understanding.

Mr. Joseph Havens; Commonwealth Press designer, gathering batches of typed copy, handwritten scrawl and 400 separate photos into a coherent whole.

Mr. Norman LeDuc; Commonwealth Press publisher, holding me to my promised deadlines.

Mrs. Judy Wilson; collector's friend, not allowing me to get sloppy as I made the fourth and fifth frustrating change on an entry.

Mrs. Marjorie Baston and Mr. Prescott (Woody) Baston, Jr.; "getting it all together."

And finally, I humbly acknowledge the assistance of Prescott Baston. His life work, as described in this Guide, needs no further embellishment.

Dr. Glenn S. Johnson
Acton, Massachusetts
December, 1979

INDEX

THE HISTORY OF SEBASTIAN MINIATURES

Historian J. P. O'Donnell writes, "The gap between the generations, unless it is to become a chasm and make history meaningless, must be bridged. Each generation owes an after-action report to the generation that follows."

In the case of Prescott Baston and his Sebastian Miniatures, the term "after-action" is partially misleading. After over 40 years of creative and productive toil, the "action" has never been as active. Mr. Baston spends today's hours sculpting, training craftsmen and lecturing all over the country. He works as hard today as he has ever worked. And the number of collectors who prize his work far outnumbers the people who have collected over all the years from 1938 to 1976.

But the generation gap *does* exist. Baston was born in 1909, the year William Howard Taft took office as President of the United States. The federal income tax (the 16th Amendment to the Constitution) was ratified four years later. In 1917, when Baston was eight, the U.S. entered World War I.

He was a 20-year-old art student in Boston at the time of the Wall Street Crash, an event plunging our country into a ten-year Great Depression. These are *not* the times of most of us. The majority of our current population was born after the Depression. Most of us do not remember those harsh years and thus cannot even hope to feel what that America was like. We were not yet a world power.

Yet strangely, and perhaps this helps to explain our current fascination with Sebastian Miniatures, Prescott Baston somehow bridges the gap. In 1938, the year he fashioned his first miniatures, Lisa Meitner, Otto Hahn and Fritz Strassman produced the first nuclear fission of uranium, an event that certainly *is* of this time. He married

Marjorie Keyes at the beginning of our entry into World War II. And who need elaborate on the aftermath in our lives of that still-incredible event?

We could recite more dates and events, but the point is already clear. With the Sebastian Miniatures, the creation of one man, we have a theme developed in one America, then nurtured through a period of great transition, and now celebrated and honored by an entirely new generation of Americans. It is our conclusion that this living bridge to the past is the essential appeal of Sebastian Miniatures.

They began innocently enough. A woman who owned the old Shaker Glen House in Woburn, Massachusetts, wanted to give mementoes of her restaurant to her diners. She knew a young man in her church who was both a practicing artist and a miniature model maker. One day, following church services, she approached the man and asked him if he could produce a small figurine that she could give away or sell.

It was 1938, and the country was still very much in the throes of the Depression. The young man, Prescott Baston, had taken many different jobs over the last several years, and he took this one.

Using his sculpting, mold-making and painting skills in his Arlington home basement, he produced a pair of miniature figurines, "Shaker Man" and Shaker Lady." The woman liked them and ordered 25 sets. To Baston's surprise and elation, she came back two weeks later and ordered another 40 sets. An idea and life work was begun.

Prescott W. Baston was born March 17, 1909, in Arlington, Massachusetts. His artistic skills were possibly inherited. That is a philosophical/scientific question much open to debate. But these skills were certainly instilled and nurtured. His father was an architectural and landscape miniaturist for Olmstead Brothers, the prestigious firm that had designed New York's Central Park and Cloisters and Boston's Public Gardens. An architectural miniaturist takes massive buildings and tracts of land and reduces them to tiny yet distinguishable objects. The young Baston spent much time working on his own miniature objects, first in imitation of his father and then in growing self-interest and self-awareness.

Upon graduation from Arlington High School, he enrolled at Boston's Vesper George School of Art. Here he completed his formal schooling in design, color and the working of many different media: paint, clay, plaster, rubber, metal and wood.

Shaker Lady **(SML 2)** and Shaker Man **(SML 1)**

These miniature figurines are the first Sebastian Miniatures. Designed in the dress of the New England religious sect, the miniatures were given to diners at the Shaker Glen House restaurant in Woburn, Massachusetts (closed in the early 1950's).

Upon leaving school during the nadir of the Depression, he quickly learned his first lesson in artistic economics: if an artist cannot work he's not an artist. Happily, he had work.

One job was with Olmstead Brothers. Like his father, he created finely-detailed scale models of building and surroundings. Another, in dramatic contrast, was his acceptance of free-lance commissions, designing and painting huge murals on various building projects, some of them federally-funded.

During all this, he continued to pursue his other favorite pastime, reading and study. He read and re-read all of Dickens. Shakespeare, Twain, Irving and Hawthorne occupied his spare time. He continued his childhood preoccupation with museums, both art and historical. When the Shaker Glen House commission entered his life, he was thoroughly qualified to design miniature figurines depicting many themes, literary and historical. And he was ready to work.

Following the continuing success of the Shaker couple, Baston began to work in 1938 and 1939 on a series of historical couples. George and Martha Washington, John and Priscilla Alden, Daniel and Mrs. Boone.

But he needed retail outlets for these miniatures. After talking to some store owners, he realized he had two problems. First, he was an American manufacturer. In 1938, the figurine gift and collectible industry as we know it did not exist. A few porcelain figurines such as Royal Dolton, Bing and Grondahl and Meissen had been imported into this country. The first Hummel figurines had been introduced to the U.S. through Marshall Field & Company three years before. The market that did exist expected European products. In stark contrast to the immigrants of the early 1900's, Baston "Europeanized" his American studio to "Sebastian." With this name, he could partly obscure the fact that his figurines were American in design and production.

His other problem was that his figurines were made of Ceramastone instead of the traditional fired porcelain. One of Baston's artistic heroes was John Rogers, the sculptor who cast 12 to 18-inch high scenes into white Ceramastone. Roger's earliest accounts of his refusal to cast his work into fired porcelain ex-

Prescott Baston, age 30, in his first studio, his home basement in Arlington, Massachusetts. Some of the early Sebastian Miniatures can be seen on the shelves in the upper right. The wall decor, rear left, was an experiment that was never successful.

plain his artistic philosophy. Rogers simply wanted the common man to be able to afford his work and decorate his home with it. Baston adopted this philosophy and refused to cast his work into the more expensive porcelain medium.

The personable young man and his line of painted Sebastian Miniatures was accepted by Olsen's, on Brattle Street in Cambridge, his first retail outlet. Others followed. By the end of 1941, his labors had produced a small business in his basement studio, a line of 16 pairs of miniature figurines and about 20 retail stores in the immediate Boston area. World War II then imposed a forced four-year absence from the main operation of his Studio.

Baston immediately volunteered his skills to the war effort. He worked at the Massachusetts Institute of Technology's Radiation Labs. But the Sebastian Miniatures continued to sell throughout the war. Retail stores needed the product, and the situation evolved to where Marjorie ran the business. Not only did she keep the books, she also supervised the five to 20 workers (depending on the season) who came into the Baston basement to make more molds, cast, clean and paint the Sebastian Miniatures. Today, Marjorie Baston minimizes her role. "The mold-makers, the casting people, the painters . . . they all called me 'boss.' Actually, they knew they were the boss. Even the paperwork seemed to know who was in charge." Prescott Baston disagrees. "The studio ran like clockwork."

The year 1945 marked three events: the end of World War II; the birth of the Bastons' son, Prescott, Jr.; and the full-speed-ahead signal for Sebastian Miniatures. From August, 1945, to March, 1946, Baston re-established the old retail outlets and established several more. The orders started coming in in their pre-war magnitude, then exceeding it. By the middle of 1946, Baston realized that production facilities had to expand. He purchased a home and a two-story building in Marblehead, Massachusetts. Marjorie settled the home and Prescott converted the other building into Sebastian Studios.

During all of this, Baston designed the bulk of his Dickens collection: David and Dora Copperfield and Mr. Micawber; Bob Cratchit, Tiny Tim and Scrooge; Sairey Gamp and the mysterious Mrs. Harris. Along with the couples of 1938 and 1939, a Children's Band he had designed in 1942 and the Dickens figures, Baston completed 1946 with 46 miniatures in the retail line. The fact that the 46 were divided into and advertised as three collectible series (Famous Couples, Children's Band, Dickens' Family), indicates an early theme that far pre-dated today's "collectible grouping" concept.

In 1947, the Shawmut Bank commissioned Baston to create a three-dimensional miniature of their trademark, the Shawmut Indian. From 1947 through 1977, Sebastian Studios produced over 90,000 of these painted and bronzed miniatures. Used for advertising and sales promotion purposes, the Shawmut was the first of over 150 private commissions designed by Baston from 1947 to 1971. Outstanding commissions included the Jello series of caricatures and animals, the New York Museum series of "authentic Miniatures," *Readers Digest* advertising redemptions, *The New Yorker* magazine's "Eustace Tilley" and designs for several Boston area banks and trust companies.

At times, Baston would receive permission to convert some of these private commissions into the retail line after a specific promotion was concluded. If the figurine had broad appeal, he would remove the inscription on the base and sell the miniature through his dealers. Many of the private commissions were produced in very small quantities (100 or 150). These are the rarest collector's items. Many of them, like the Jello series, were produced in quantities of 3,000 to 5,000. These too are considered rare.

In 1947, Baston also began his Shakespeare series. Not only did he sculpt the popular Romeo, Juliet, Cleopatra and Mark Antony. He designed the more obscure Falstaff, Mistress Ford and Malvolio. As with his Dickens' figurines of Barkis, Sam Weller and the Parish Beadle, Baston designed his personal favorites along with the mass market subjects.

The retail line grew into the form of pen stands and paperweights in reply to the demand for functional items from his growing number of dealers. Many of his miniatures took the shape of figurine, pen stand *and* paperweight, depending on the particular request of a particular dealer.

Prescott Baston in his Marblehead studio in 1948. He is examining the mold for one of his Ceramastone castings, shown assembled on the bench at lower left.

It is impossible today to establish the exact quantities of miniatures sold through dealers from 1938 to 1976. Baston remembers that certain items sold extremely well, in the tens of thousands; miniatures such as "The Doctor," "In the Candy Store," "The Clown" and Daniel Chester French's "Lincoln Memorial." Other retail figurines such as "Gathering Tulips" were produced at the request of a single store and were produced in a quantity of a few hundred.

We must pause here to remember the times—to bridge the gap. From the period 1938 to around the mid-1950's, the collectibles market existed primarily of U.S. stamps and coins. An artist and businessman like Prescott Baston had no way of anticipating that his figurines would be sought-after collector's items in the late 1970's. He was busy creating, selling and running a studio. Final details on production runs were lost forever in the crush of activity.

And the miniatures themselves were purchased as gifts, souvenirs and even advertising promotions (much as baseball cards promoted the sale of gum and tobacco). Many were discarded and destroyed. A few were given as gifts or passed on to people who collected them. A few collectors began acquiring hundreds of the miniatures, but very few of these major collections exist.

Meanwhile, design and production in Marblehead continued.

The production process (described in detail on page 13 through 21 of this book), had formalized into mold-making, casting, cleaning, rough painting, detail painting,

Armando Carli, a man who worked with Prescott Baston at MIT during World War II, puts finishing touches to a Shawmut Indian mold in 1950. Other molds are drying in the background.

Three women work on Jello "Whales" in the early 1950's. The white castings are rough-painted by the woman in the foreground and final details are painted by the woman in the center. The woman in back prepares them for shipment.

sealing and shipping. Baston continued to train his craftsmen even as he continued to design new miniatures. In 1948 he began his Mark Twain series. The Jello series began in 1952 and ended in 1955.

In 1950, just prior to the Korean War, Baston intensified his public appearance activities. Many of his appearances were commercial ventures, educating the public on what goes into creating and producing art but directly tied-in to the Sebastian Miniatures.

He also had signed a contract with Flora Frame, a "Club Program Bureau." Again in a bridge to the past, the phenomenon of a television set in every home was still a thing of the future. Lecturers on practically every subject toured the country speaking to clubs and schools. In addition to running Sebastian Studios, Baston logged many thousands of miles lecturing to groups of all kinds.

The years passed. Baston's designs touched on deeply religious themes (the "Nativity," "Pope John the 23rd") and humorous events ("The Commons Cow," "Lady Rittenhouse Square" and "The Buffalo Bee"). He miniaturized famous works of art (Raphael's "Sistine Madonna," Durer's "Praying Hands," Rodin's "The Thinker"). He created new series (Mark Twain's Family, The Legend of Sleepy Hollow, Famous Couples). With one series, the Godey Children, Baston designed six children dressed in costumes illustrated in *Godey's Ladies Book,* a magazine spanning the Civil War years that served as the *New Yorker* of its day. But from the deeply serious to the farcical, from the planned series to the one-of-a-kind commissions, Baston continued sculpting, selling, running the studio and lecturing. The Fifties and then the Sixties passed in this manner.

In this 1950's advertising flyer, Prescott Baston's services as a lecturer are described by the Flora Frame Club Program Bureau. The flyer promises: "His masterly understanding of art and architecture . . . makes his lecture more than just a talk. In fact, it is actually a one-lesson course in the elements of design. His brilliant, instructive lectures abound with artistic insight, unusual information, human interest, and the true tang of Yankee wit and humor."

During peak periods, the Marblehead studio would hold up to 25 people doing various stages of production. Baston had separated the two types of painting skills involved. "Broad area" painting, covering the large portions of each casting, could be accomplished most efficiently by home painters. During busy times, a steady stream of local people could be seen picking-up white castings and returning painted figurines. But the outstanding characteristic of Sebastian Miniatures, the detail, could only be painted on by skilled and steady-handed artisans under close quality supervision. By 1969, Baston had

A woman paints Sebastian Miniatures at an in-store appearance at a Boston store in 1951. Then, as today, the average person is surprised at the amount of effort and skill involved in the making of practically anything.

Prescott Baston at a store appearance in 1952. Here he talks with "Mother Parker," a Boston radio station WEEI announcer. She was the model for one of a series of seven popular WEEI caricatures designed for sale in Boston.

created 392 separate miniatures and was producing for about 50 retail outlets and scores of private companies. But another gap was yet to be bridged.

In 1969, Mr. Ray Kennedy, president of the Lance Corporation in Hudson, Massachusetts, was looking for artists to sculpt works that could be cast into fine pewter. In the process of transition from an industrial foundry to an art foundry, Lance needed sculptors to help create the then-infant pewter figurine market. A native of Massachusetts himself, Kennedy asked Baston if he would be interested in accepting a commission to sculpt figurines to be sold as Hudson Pewter. As with the Shaker Glen House commission, Baston accepted and an entirely new career began for him.

Baston sculpted Hudson's "Spirit of '76" commemorative plate and many of Hudson's "Historic Americans" figures. These works were to achieve an unprecedented popularity during the years immediately preceding our Bicentennial.

Baston's "Spirit of '76" plate, designed for and cast by Hudson Pewter. During the years 1974 to 1976, over 18,000 of these plates were purchased as Bicentennial commemoratives.

Baston's interpretation of Daniel Chester French's Lincoln Memorial. This piece remains a Hudson Pewter staple.

In the same year, Kennedy met with Royal Worcester (United States) to secure a contract for manufacturing Worcester Pewter. Under the agreement, the Lance foundry would cast pewter for sale under Royal Worcester's name and through that company's distribution organization. The immediate result of this agreement was to have an impact on the newly-growing "collectibles" market. All the elements for the design, manufacture and distribution of the now-famous Royal Worcester Bicentennial plate series were in place. Prescott Baston was the designer, Lance was the manufacturer and Royal Worcester the national distributor.

As Lance and Hudson Pewter grew, so did the awareness and appreciation of Sebastian Miniatures among Lance's distribution officials. And as Baston's pewter commissions grew, so did his awareness of Lance's national marketing operation. Discussions between Kennedy and Baston developed from 1970 on and, in mid-1975, Lance and Sebastian Studios announced an agreement. Prescott Baston would train Lance craftsmen in the production of Sebastian Miniatures and would create new designs. Lance, in turn, would promote and distribute the miniatures through its national sales organization. In late 1975, a strategy of national marketing began.

Philip DeNino, Lance's design manager, and Mr. Baston selected 100 of the 244 miniatures sold through the old retail outlets. As production was transferred from Marblehead to Hudson, Mr. Baston trained scores of people in the old crafts of mold-making, casting and painting. The Marblehead Studio was closed as a production facility.

Royal Worcester's 1972 "Boston Tea Party" plate in the five-plate Bicentennial series. The plates were issued one design per year, in a limited edition of 10,000 plates, from 1972 to 1976. This plate, issued originally at $45, has a current market value of $275 (*Plate Collector*, Dec. 1, 1979).

Sebastian Studios in Marblehead. This building, from 1946 to 1976, served as headquarters and housed the craftsmen that produced the Sebastian Miniatures over the 30-year period. Mr. Baston uses it as his design studio.

Lance began by distributing the line throughout New England. The immediate appeal in Connecticut, New Hampshire and Maine precipitated the opening of dealerships in New York and Pennsylvania. By January of 1977, Sebastian Miniatures were beginning to appear in the South. Collectors who had begun their collections because of visits to Boston in the past immediately recognized what was happening. Lance began to receive the first ripples of what later was to build into a tidal wave of collector correspondence.

During the years beginning in roughly 1965, four totally distinct and separate phenomenon had been occurring parallel to the Sebastian story. First, large numbers of Americans had adopted collecting as a hobby and/or financial pursuit. Spurred first by the traditional stamps and coins, Americans began collecting a wider range of historic objects. Plates were among the first to be organized (sound collecting requires organization), but now elaborate societies and newsletters began to be formed for the gathering and dissemination of information on practically everything from advertising posters to barbed wire to beer cans to baseball cards to, yes, figurines with a history. Sebastian Miniatures had an over-40-year history.

Second, Americans were becoming increasingly involved with miniaturization. The number of people who now build and collect 1:12 scale dollhouses and furniture has placed this interest in the Top Ten of craft hobbies. Although not purporting to be 1:12 scale, the Sebastian Miniatures *are* miniature.

Third, in a new wave of nostalgia that looks back for basic roots, Americans have sought out their past in rapidly increasing numbers. Just as nuclear energy, miniature data processors and the electronic media touch our lives, so too does our appreciation of our past. The art of Norman Rockwell has never been as popular as it is today. Our search for "Roots" is not a uniquely black-American experience. And Sebastian Miniatures *do* tell us of our past.

Finally, Americans have become increasingly "America conscious." Prescott Baston is experiencing a complete reversal of his late 1930's situation when he had to make his work appear European to achieve validity. And Sebastian Miniatures are made in America by an American.

All of the above coincided in July and August of 1978. After modest tests in New England, the Eastern Seaboard and the South, the Sebastian Miniatures were introduced nationally.

Anyone serving the American marketplace will agree that at times, strange and unexplainable situations will coincide to produce unexpected results. Dramatic examples are the failure of Ford's Edsel and the success of the movie "Star Wars" with all generations. Lesser examples are a very crowded restaurant on a night when there really should be no crowds. One sage marketing man, having enjoyed his "successes" and having survived his "failures," describes these results as "lunar phenomena." "I might as well have consulted my Tarot cards or the birth rate in Bombay for all the careful planning I had done," he concludes.

Neither Lance nor Prescott Baston were ready for the "lunar phenomenon" of July and August, 1978. Orders from collectors and dealers poured into Hudson. A four-week delivery lengthened into eight and then 12 weeks. Finally, in September, a moratorium was placed on all new dealerships and orders.

Lance's internal staff stared at orders stacked on the floor. Production in Hudson was expanded and a group of craftspeople on Martha's Vineyard (an island off the coast of mainland Massachusetts) was pressed into service. In February, 1979, Lance opened a new production facility in Lee, New Hampshire, exclusively devoted to Sebastian Miniatures. Determined to maintain the quality standards of the past, Baston trained trainers who supervised the training of still more craftsmen. In July, 1978, 40 people in Hudson produced Sebastian Miniatures. By July, 1979, over 400 people were involved.

Baston produced two figures ("Sidewalk Days") that were designed in 1938 but were never sold. Limited to 10,000 sets, the pair sold out in months. He was asked by the Rockport Art Association to help raise funds to rebuild Motif No. 1, the fisherman's shack that had been destroyed in the February snowstorm of 1978. The shack was so titled because it is reputed to be the most-painted subject in America. Baston agreed and designed a pewter-rimmed Motif #1 plate limited to 10,000. The plate sold out. During the Fall of 1979, Prescott Baston has appeared at 17 separate collector shows and stores in 12 states, climaxed by Walt Disney World's Thanksgiving celebration in Orlando, Florida.

And this is only the beginning. Only now are Americans, previously unfamiliar with the Sebastian story, beginning to discover and collect this over-40-year-old expression of a man's life. We are still in the "lunar phenomenon" stage. The future is unpredictable in terms of the extent to which Sebastian Miniatures will become part and parcel of our American heritage.

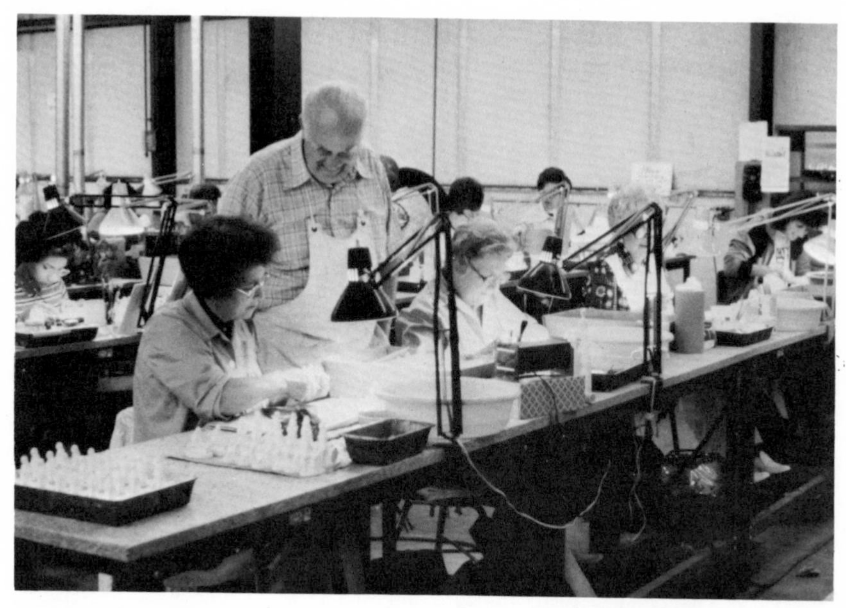

Prescott Baston monitors the work of several women cleaning inperfections from castings before they are painted. The photo was taken in Hudson.

Prescott Baston is alive and well, embarked on yet another stage of his career. The old established collectors, to a person, are pleased with the national acceptance of work they have so long cherished. As of this writing, authorized dealerships are coming aboard daily, intrigued by the ground swell of this collecting event.

It would seem, in restrospect, that a whole new dimension has been added to a philosophy penned by Prescott Baston in 1948. "Two goals have guided my work through the years. First, to do the most honest portrayals I can. Second, to create scenes so appealing that other people immediately experience a sense of pleasure from them."

HOW SEBASTIAN MINIATURES ARE MADE

Prescott Baston began making his Sebastian Miniatures in his Arlington, Massachusetts home. From 1938 to 1946, as many as 20 people at one time were involved in their production there. Operations shifted to Marblehead from 1946 to 1976. Now Sebastian Miniatures are produced in Hudson and Martha's Vineyard, Massachusetts, and Lee, New Hampshire.

Prescott Baston remains the sole sculptor of all new figurines. Now, as in 1938, he trains master craftsmen to supervise all production. In this pictorial essay, Baston was photographed in his old Marblehead studio.

Step 1. *"First I get an idea for a grouping. Something that strikes my fancy. What usually strikes my fancy is something historical, turn-of-the-century. Then I study up on particulars, such as clothing and accessories that I've decided to build into the scene. First I work in the general, trying to catch a tilt of the head or putting several figures together in a pleasant way."*

Step 2. *"I add more clay as the idea grows. Finally, I'm finished with the clay. All of the shape is there but practically none of the fine detailing."*

Step 3. *"Then I start to prepare the mold. I stick thin metal fins into the clay to provide natural parting lines for the two-piece mold."*

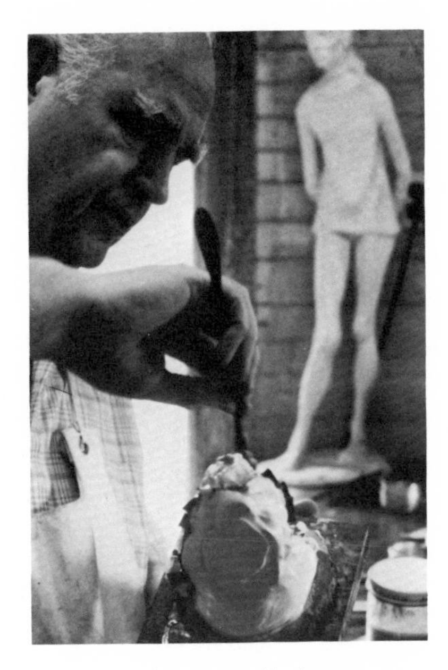

Step 4. *"I begin a mold-making process very similar to the one used in bronze casting. I spread a coat of blue plaster evenly over the clay sculpture."*

Step 5. *"Then I apply, one, two and sometimes three coats of white plaster over the blue. This builds up the mold material around the clay to give it strength."*

Step 6. *"When the plaster has hardened, I pull the mold off the clay inside. The mold separates where I had placed the metal fins. This step usually destroys the original clay."*

Step 7. *"Then I apply a release agent that activates the blue color lining the interior of the plaster mold."*

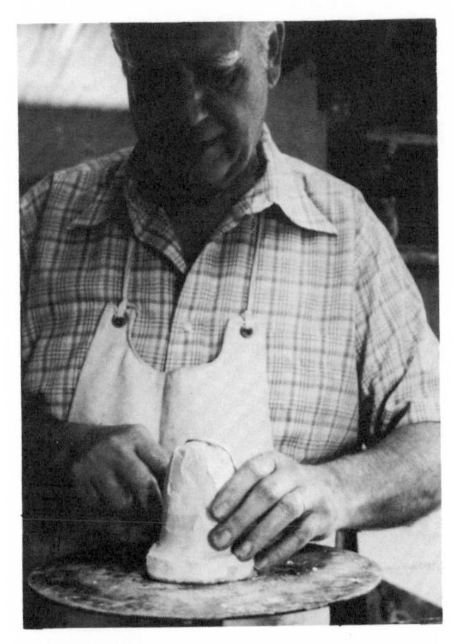

Step 8. *"I strap the mold segments back together. This forms a cavity that is now the mirror image of the original sculpting."*

Step 9. *"I pour a mixture of liquid Ceramastone into the mold. The liquid hardens until the plaster mold and the Ceramastone figurine are one solid mass, separated from each other only by the blue agent."*

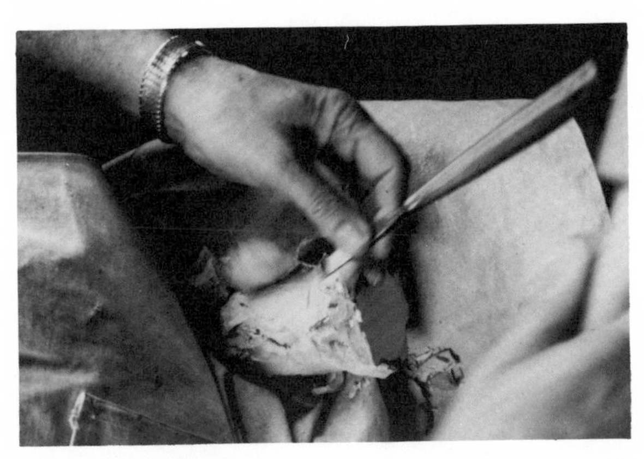

Step 10. *"I cut away the outer mold of plaster. When I get to the blue, I know I'm close to the figurine. The result of all this is a fairly rough, slightly oversized Sebastian Miniature."*

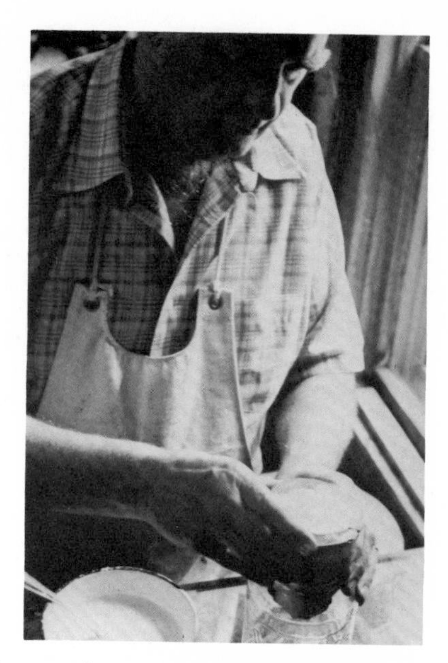

Step 11. *"Working with this casting and sharp tools, I carve the final detail into the miniature. Detail on the buttons, nose, cheekbones. Then smaller details, like an insignia on a duffel bag or initials carved into a school desk."*

Step 12. *"I use a liquid rubber that hardens into a mold tight enough to capture the original detail, yet pliable enough to be used again. When this rubber mold is pulled, I can use it many times to cast miniatures. I use the same Ceramastone for my production miniatures as I do for my masters."*

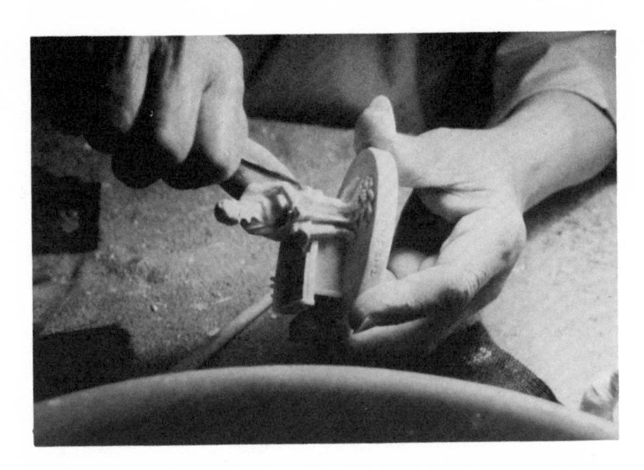

Step 13. *"The result of this casting is a white, hard Ceramastone miniature that has to be hand-cleaned with a knife to remove the mold separation lines. With this, the sculpting, mold-making, casting and cleaning processes are completed. The miniature is ready for painting."*

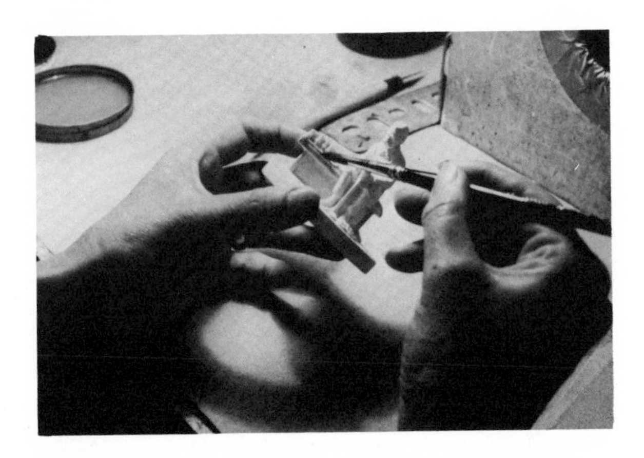

Step 14. *"I paint the large areas of the miniature such as benches and clothing with a fairly large brush."*

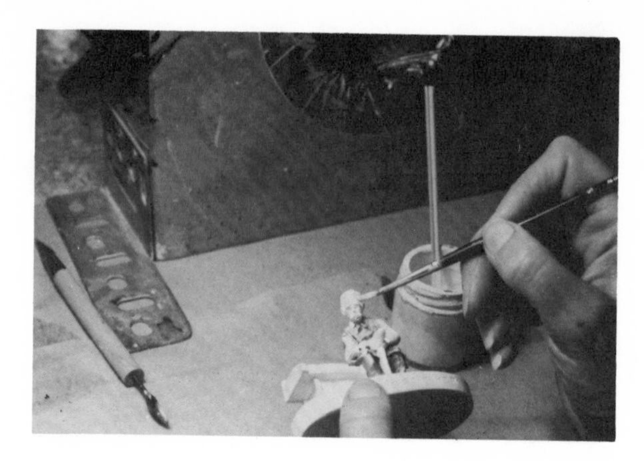

Step 15. *"I paint the more detailed areas such as hands and faces with a smaller brush."*

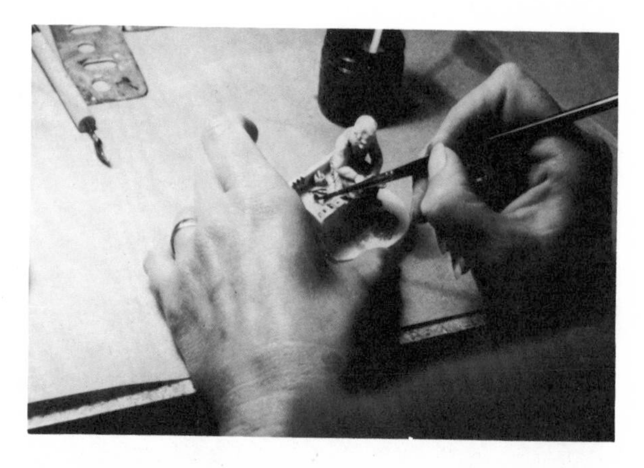

Step 16. *"Then, using a brush with just a few hairs, I add the final details. Details such as the Shoemaker's tools, eyebrows and blue eyes."*

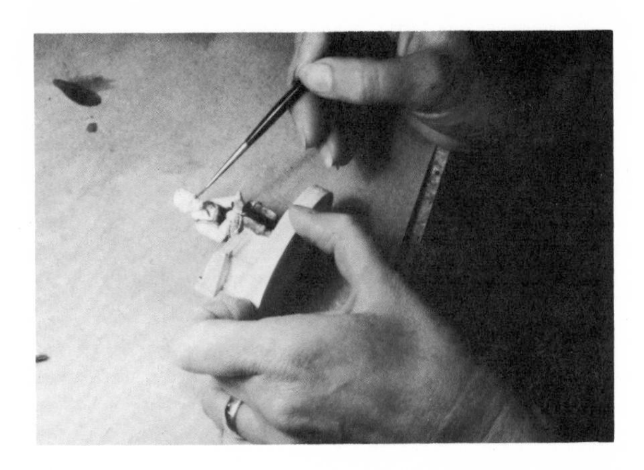

Step 17. *"I apply a special sealant to protect the color and also give the miniature an appealing gloss finish. When this is done, the miniature is completed, ready for packaging and shipping."*

NOTES ON THE COLLECTION

SML—SEBASTIAN MINIATURE LISTING

A chronological number is assigned to each figurine and plaque. "SML 1" denotes "Shaker Man," the first Sebastian; "SML 411" denotes "Snow Days—Boy," the last as of December, 1979. These numbers are permanently assigned.

PRODUCTION STATUS

Four designations are used to list the various production statuses of all 411 Sebastian Miniatures. These are Open Editions, Limited Editions, SSR and Private.

OPEN

Since Lance began national distribution of Sebastian Miniatures, 113 models have been selected from Mr. Baston's original 265 designed since 1938 for his retail dealers. These, plus the new miniatures designed since 1976, have been sold through Lance's expanded distribution organization. They are available to collectors through Authorized Sebastian Dealers.

LIMITED EDITIONS

Beginning in 1978, Lance has introduced 14 limited edition figurines. Six of them are limited by quantity and eight by year of production. Of the six limited by quantity, three sets of "Childhood Days" pairs were limited to 10,000. "Sidewalk Days" (issued in 1978) are sold-out. "Building Days" was issued in 1979 and "Snow Days" in 1980.

Of the eight limited by year-of-production, "Paul Bunyan" was retired forever in 1978 and "The Clown" in 1979. "George Washington" will be retired October 31, 1980.

A new series, "America Remembers," was introduced in 1979. Depicting a family of four in turn-of-the-century costume and pastime, "Family Sing" was retired on December 31, 1979. "Family Picnic" will be retired December 31, 1980.

Prescott Baston designed a plaque for his original dealers to use as display signs in their store. Lance retired this first plaque in December, 1978. A new version, with minor modifications in the poster copy, was retired in 1979. A still-new version will be retired December 31, 1980. All three plaques have become collector items.

SSR *(Sebastian Studio Retail)*

When Lance made its selection of 113 miniatures to continue in production, over 150 miniatures designed for Mr. Baston's original retail stores were discontinued. Castings and molds are maintained and stored, but are not available to today's collector. These are rare miniatures, available only through the collectible resale market.

PRIVATE

Over 150 Sebastian Miniatures were designed and produced by Prescott Baston for private and commercial use. These pieces bear the designation of the sponsoring firm on the base (i.e., "It's Time for Jello," "Johnson and Johnson," "Shawmut Bank," etc.). In some cases, the sponsoring corporation released their rights to the design after a promotion was over. If the figure had a broad subject appeal, Baston removed the inscribed base and cast a blank base for sale in the retail line. For example, the "Nurse" designed for Mead-Johnson in 1956, became Sebastian Studio's "Nurse" in 1967. The figurine bearing the Mead-Johnson inscription is an extremely rare miniature.

QUANTITIES

Three quantity designations are listed in the Collection: Open, SSR and Private.

OPEN

Except for limited editions, no quantities are published on open editions. They are available to every collector and, except for retired pieces, will remain available.

SSR

Mr. Baston did not keep detailed records of the quantities he sold through his retail stores prior to 1976. He remembers the most popular figurines ("Doctor," "Little Mother," "Bob Cratchit and Tiny Tim"), but the rest are lost in a maze of sculpting, production schedules and selling. For the purposes of this Guide, it is safe to say that all quantities of figurines designated "SSR" are very low in comparison to today's collectible market.

PRIVATE

Prescott Baston has a remarkable memory. In preparing this Guide, he recited the events surrounding a particular promotion, names of the people involved, how the figurines were used and approximately how many.

Some promotions were broad and long-lasting. Around 90,000 Shawmut Indians were made over the years. Some quantities were very low. "Doc Berry" was produced for Doctor Berry's birthday in order to help him raise funds for his boys' camp in Maine. In all cases, the quantities listed for Private commissions are accurate.

DATES

Two factors must be discussed under the heading of dating; Copyright vs. Issue Year and Year Produced.

COPYRIGHT VS. ISSUE YEAR

In all cases, an open Sebastian Miniature will include the year of copyright cast into its base. Most of the SSR and Private pieces also include this copyright year. In most cases, the copyright year is the year the miniature was issued and sold. In a few exceptions, a piece was modified and re-copyrighted. In other cases, a piece was designed and then not issued until later. In either case, all dates listed in the Guide are the years the miniatures were first issued to the public.

YEAR PRODUCED

Prior to 1978, Sebastian Miniatures bore a green and silver label affixed to the bottom of the base. In 1978, a green paper label replaced the old. In 1979 a blue label was used and in 1980 a yellow label. Any figurine listed under "SSR" and "Private" was produced prior to 1976.

In November, 1978, the "costume" (broad area) painters were asked to initial the base of the miniatures. A typical signature will appear "JP/a/2." This means:

JP Joanne Priest, painter
a Year painted
a 1979
b 1980
2. Where painted
1. Lee, New Hampshire studio
2. Hudson studio
3. Martha's Vineyard studio

This signature is preserved under a tight sealant.

SEBASTIAN MINIATURE FORMS

Seven forms of Sebastian Miniatures exist:

FIGURINES

These are single figures ("Shaker Man," "Abraham Lincoln," etc.) cast on a small base, usually round.

SCENES

These are single figures with design accessories ("Doctor," "Becky Thatcher"); several figures ("Little Sister," "Little Nell and Grandfather") or several figures and design accessories ("Nativity," "Family Sing"). In all cases, a scene tells a story.

PEN STANDS

Many SSR and Private commission designs include a penholder cast into the base. No pen stands are in production at this time.

PAPERWEIGHTS

Several SSR and Private commissions positioned figurines and scenes on a heavy raised platform. Two paperweight forms are "Ben Franklin at the Printing Press" and "Lincoln Memorial."

PLAQUES

Prescott Baston designed several plaques. Plaques incorporate a design element with a poster space for a display or advertising message (Private commission). The Sebastian Collector's Plaque is available through authorized dealers.

PLATES

Sebastian Studios issued its first limited edition plate in 1978, the "Motif No. 1." Rimmed in Lance pewter, it was the first of four plates issued thus far: "Grand Canyon" (1979), "Lone Cypress" (1980) and "In the Candy Store" (1980). Since these plates are in a new form, they were not included in the Guide. They are, however, part and parcel of Prescott Baston's ongoing art.

BELLS

Limited edition "Dickens' Christmas Carol" bells were introduced in 1979 ("Bob Cratchit and Tiny Tim"). The bell is handblown, while the figurine handle is pressed crystal. The "Scrooge" bell is issued in 1980. The bells, like the plates, are not included in this Guide.

SEBASTIAN MINIATURES COLLECTORS SOCIETY

We collectors want information on our collection. We also want to be assured that the objects of our collecting are carefully controlled. For these two reasons, the new Sebastian Miniatures Collectors Society was organized in Hudson.

The Society serves as the gatherer and publisher of information. A quarterly Newsletter discusses Prescott Baston's activities, plus information on existing and growing collections.

It serves as a clearinghouse, putting collectors in touch with one another for purposes of correspondence, comparison or resale.

It serves as an advisory board, planning, with Mr. Baston, new designs and series, permanent retirement of pieces, cataloging and revision of the Guide.

Finally, it serves a function no one can predict. The Society answers those personal questions, peculiar to each individual collector, that are important but not covered in the Guide and Newsletters. When these questions occur, write, with your Membership number to:

Mrs. Judy Wilson, Acting Director
Sebastian Miniatures Collectors Society
321 Central Street
Hudson, Massachusetts 01749

THE COLLECTION

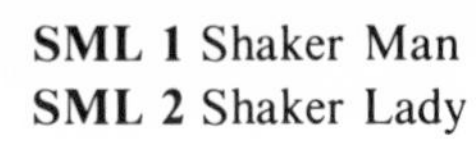

SML 1 Shaker Man
SML 2 Shaker Lady *1938/SSR*

"These were the first. They started the whole thing."

SML 3 George Washington
SML 4 Martha Washington *1938/SSR*

"George was taken from a youthful portrait, and Martha from a portrait painted after her marriage to George."

SML 5 John Alden
SML 6 Priscilla *1938/SSR*

"Priscilla is at her spinning wheel. John is presenting the proposal of Miles Standish for her hand."

SML 7 Williamsburg Governor
SML 8 Williamsburg Lady *1939/SSR*

"The colony of Williamsburg was very stylish. The Governor and Lady are fashionably dressed."

SML 9 Ben Franklin
SML 10 Deborah Franklin *1939/SSR*

"Ben is shown as he might have appeared at debate and Deborah is shown with what might have been a piece of knitting for one of their many children."

SML 11 Gabriel
SML 12 Evangeline *1939/SSR*

"They are from Longfellow's poem Evangeline."

SML 13 Coronado
SML 14 Coronado's Senora *1939/SSR*

"These are among the early settlers of the West Coast."

SML 15 Sam Houston
SML 16 Margaret Houston *1939/SSR*

"Sam is shown after his appearance in Texas."

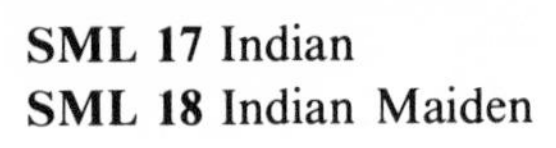

SML 17 Indian
SML 18 Indian Maiden *1939/SSR*

"The maiden is shown with a papoose on her back while the Indian sits at the fireside."

SML 19 John Lafitte
SML 20 Catherine Lafitte *1939/SSR*

"The pirate John Lafitte is shown with his sword between his hands and Catherine with a basket of groceries on her shoulder."

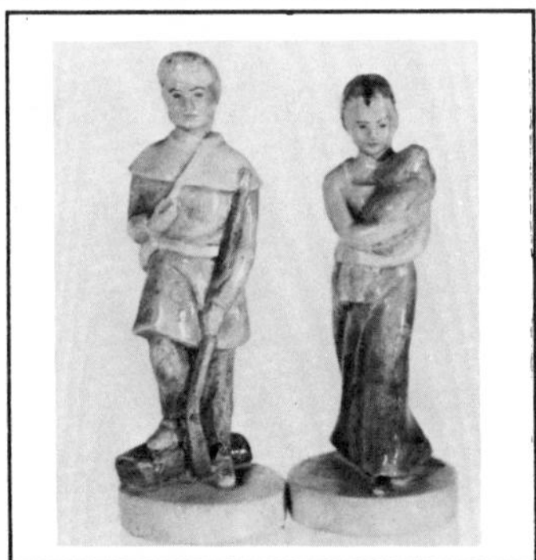

SML 21 Daniel Boone
SML 22 Mrs. Boone *1939/SSR*

"Daniel is shown on one of his exploring expeditions while his wife is at home with one of their children."

SML 23 Peter Stuyvesant
SML 24 Annie Stuyvesant *1939/SSR*

"The Dutch Governor of New York and his wife are dressed in traditional Dutch costumes."

SML 25 John Harvard
SML 26 Mrs. Harvard *1939/SSR*

"He is dressed in his academic robes and she is standing at his side."

Not available for photography

SML 27 John Smith
SML 28 Pocahontas *1939/SSR*

"John is dressed in his armor. Pocahontas is walking toward him prior to saving his life."

SML 29 William Penn
SML 30 Mrs. Penn *1939/SSR*

"The first Governor of Pennsylvania is holding the royal charter to that State. His wife is standing at his side."

SML 31 Buffalo Bill
SML 32 Annie Oakley *1939/SSR*

"They are shown with their carbines, having been at a shooting match. These were my last designs before World War II."

CHILDREN'S BAND *SSR*

"I designed these as children's gifts during the war."

SML 33 Majorette *1942/SSR*
SML 34 Cymbals *1942/SSR*
SML 35 Horn *1942/SSR*
SML 36 Accordian *1942/SSR*
SML 37 Tuba *1942/SSR*
SML 38 Drum *1942/SSR*

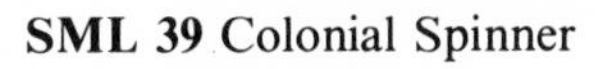

SML 39 Colonial Spinner *1946/1000*

"I made this for a candy company as a promotional item. It was my first private commission with the miniatures after the Shakers."

SML 40 Farmer *1946/Open (6226)*

"I made this for retail distribution before I started the Dickens figures."

SML 41 Micawber *1946/Open (6101)*

"A ne'er do well from David Copperfield *is shown planning some big project."*

SML 42 Mr. Pickwick *1946/Open (6106)*

"Shown making notes on his theory of tittlebats."

SML 43 David and Dora Copperfield *1946/Open (6102)*

"David Copperfield and his first wife are leaving the church after their wedding."

SML 44 Sam Weller *1946/Open (6107)*

"Seated on a pile of hay polishing boots. He originated the saying 'Ask him if he wants them now, or will he wait until he gets them'."

SML 45 Aunt Betsy Trotwood *1946/Open (6103)*

"David Copperfield's aunt is carrying her umbrella and rushing to the front yard to scare off the tourists riding on donkeys."

SML 46 Sairey Gamp and Mrs. Harris (packaged as set) *1946/Open (6108)*

"Sairey Gamp and Mrs. Harris (who is an imaginary character and represented by an empty base) are shown together. Mrs. Harris, the imaginary character, is the only person who will speak well of Sairey Gamp and Sairey quotes her often."

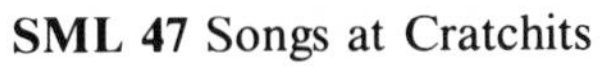

SML 47 Songs at Cratchits *1946/Open (6113)*

"Three of the Cratchit children are enthusiastically singing Christmas songs at Tiny Tim's home."

SML 48 Mrs. Cratchit *1946/Open (6114)*

"Mrs. Cratchit, wearing 'a twice-turned gown made brave with a six pence worth of ribbon,' is bringing the tiny plum pudding to the dining room."

SML 49 Bob Cratchit and Tiny Tim *1946/Open (6111)*

"Shown returning from church. Tim is seated on his father's shoulder and the father is decorated with 'six foot of scarf exclusive of fringe'."

SML 50 Scrooge *1946/Open (6112)*

"Scrooge is holding an account book to calculate what some victim owes him."

SML 51 Peggotty *1946/Open (6104)*

"Peggotty is seated on a trunk digging refreshment out of a picnic basket and popping buttons off the back of her dress as she always did when excited."

SML 52 Barkis *1946/Open (6105)*

"The local truckman is wearing his coat with 'a collar so high it pushes his hat forward, sleeves so long his hands disappear and red glass buttons.' Later he proposed to Peggotty by sending a message by David Copperfield: 'Barkis is willin'."

SML 53 Dickens' Cottage *1946/Open (6116)*

"Designed as a backdrop for the Dickens collection."

SML 54 The Lobsterman *1947/Open (6201)*

"Shown taking lobsters from a trap that is balanced on the gunwhale of his boat.

SML 55 Sampling the Stew *1947/SSR*
(Paperweight)

"This is a New England lady sampling a lobster stew which is cooking on her black iron stove. It was formerly entitled 'Yankee Kitchen'. It's retitled under duress from Texas."

SML 56 Sampling the Stew *1947/Open (6202)*

"Redesigned as a figurine."

SML 57 R. H. Stearns Couple *1947/1,500*

"Shows a young couple leaving the Stearns store with an elaborate package. For the store's 100th anniversary."

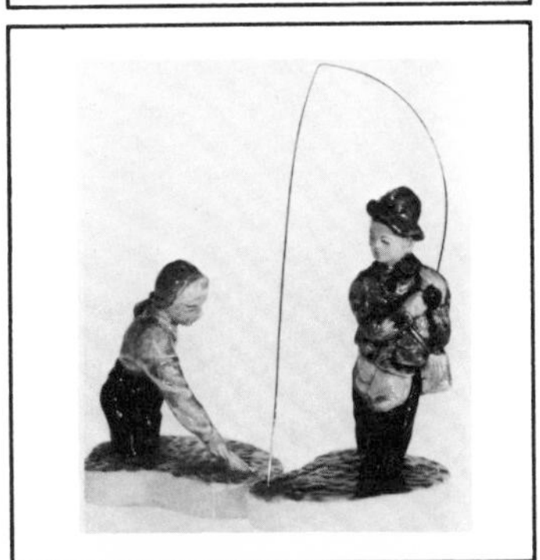

SML 58 Fisherman *1947/Fisherman Open (6506)*
SML 59 Fisherman's Wife *Fisherman's Wife/SSR*

"A fisherman, wading in a trout stream, has apparently made a catch. His wife is in the same stream, about to net the fish."

SML 60 Fisherman and Wife (Pen Stand) *1947/SSR*

"I started casting designs into pen stands at the request of some Boston stationery stores."

SML 61 In the Candy Store *1947/Open (6221)*

"Made originally for the Necco Candy Company. A young girl is making her first purchase of penny candy. The store owner is handing her the paper sack and her mother is watching approvingly."

SML 62 In the Candy Store (Pen Stand) *1947/2,000*

SML 63 Abraham Lincoln *1947/Open (6002)*

"Mr. Lincoln is wearing his grey shawl about his shoulders and has apparently been searching his Bible for reassurance."

SML 64 Outboard Motor Couple *1947/Open (6507)*

"This figure was designed for an insurance company to indicate the advantages of a pension program.

SML 65 Howard Johnson's Pieman *1947/300*

"This is the trademark of Howard Johnson's restaurant chain. It shows the pieman in Colonial costume with a little boy making a purchase."

SML 66 George Washington and Cannon *1947/ Open; Discontinued Forever Oct. 31, 1980. (6001)*

"The General is shown in his uniform standing before a Revolutionary cannon."

SML 67 Franklin D. Roosevelt *1947/SSR*

"President Roosevelt is on the bridge of a naval vessel. He is wearing his Admiral's cape and is standing beside the ship's compass to guide him in the right direction."

SML 68 Princess Elizabeth *1947/2,000*

"Shown dressed in her wedding gown at the ceremony which occurred in 1947. This was an important event, and we sold about 2,000 figurines that year."

SML 69 Lieut. Philip Mountbatten *1947/2,000*

"Shown in the naval uniform he wore for his marriage to Princess Elizabeth."

SML 70 Toll House Town Crier *1947/4,000*

"This figurine was made for the Toll House restaurant and was used for advertising purposes."

SML 71 Toll House Town Crier *1947/2,000*
(Pen Stand)

(Dated on stand by year of promotion).

SML 72 The Pilgrims *1947/1,500*

"Also made for the Toll House restaurant for advertising purposes."

The next four figures were made in collaboration with Francis Dahl, cartoonist for the Boston Herald.

SML 73 Mrs. Beacon Hill (Dahl) *1947/SSR*

"This figure, whose name in Mr. Dahl's cartoons was Salton-Cabot, is shown waiting under the clock at the R. H. Stearns Company. Her husband is taking her to lunch at the Waldorf. She has the inevitable umbrella."

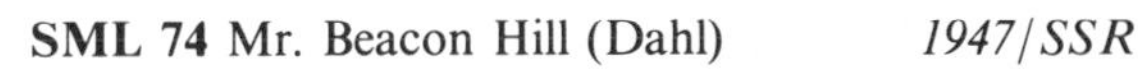

SML 74 Mr. Beacon Hill (Dahl) *1947/SSR*

"He is proceeding across the Boston Commons with his umbrella and with his green baize bag which Bostonians of Harvard extraction carry. A squirrel is on one side and two pigeons on the other."

SML 75 Dilemma—The Boston Commons Cow (Dahl) *1947/SSR*

"Commemorates the privilege of a few Beacon Hill families to pasture a cow on the Commons. Rumor had it that she was posed in front of the State house because there was so much bull inside."

SML 76 The Fisherman (Dahl) *1947/SSR*

"This nautical character is posed holding a rather large fish which is conveniently placed so he can lean his pipe on it."

SML 77 The Farmer's Wife *1947/Open (6227)*

"The farmer's wife is sitting on the back steps peeling apples and tossing the peelings to a couple of hens."

SML 78 Amish Folk *1947/Open (6225)*

"Shows a lady with a market basket and her young son who is making a desperate effort to keep his big black hat on straight."

SML 79 Amish Man *1947/Open (6224)*

"This dignified farmer is dressed in his traditional somber garb."

SML 80 Henry VIII *1947/SSR*

"This character is shown in the costume of the Holbein portrait."

SML 81 Anne Boleyn *1947/SSR*

"She is in a black gown with an elaborate conical headdress and flowing orange decoration. Her right hand covers her left because of the deformity of her left hand."

SML 82 Falstaff *1947/SSR*

"This ponderous warrior is posed in such a manner, or so he thinks, as to be irresistible to the members of the opposite sex."

SML 83 Mistress Ford *1947/SSR*

"The leading character of The Merry Wives of Windsor *is obviously plotting to get the better of the offensive Falstaff."*

SML 84 Romeo *1947/SSR*

"This youthful lover chose a combination of gallantry and belligerence that characterized the part he played in Shakespeare's theatrical family."

SML 85 Juliet *1947/SSR*

"Is romantically looking forward to the ball during which she meets Romeo."

SML 86 The Shawmut Indian *1947/90,000*

"This is the first version of the miniature of the National Shawmut Bank's trademark, made specifically for the bank's customers. This and later versions reached the total of more than 90,000 pieces."

SML 87 Little Nell and her Grandfather *1948/ Open (6110)*

"Shown traveling the back country of England. His passion for gambling caused them to lose their store and their home. They are now living from day to day with Little Nell the breadwinner and her grandfather wasting her earnings at every stop."

SML 88 Pecksniff *1948/Open (6109)*

"The self-righteous villain is standing in complacent dignity beside the model bust he has made of himself. His attitude of righteousness is a disguise for his avaricious character."

SML 89 Judge Thatcher *1948/Open (6134)*

"This gentleman is the local politician and civic leader of the Tom Sawyer-Huckleberry Finn stories. He preceded my Mark Twain series by a few months." *(See SML 108-112).*

SML 90 Slalom *1948/SSR*

"This is a skier executing a turn in his slalom race."

SML 91 Sitzmark *1948/SSR*

"This is a young lady skier who has ended up sitting in the snow and making a sitzmark."

SML 92 The Observer (Jordan Marsh) *1948/8,000*

"The Jordan Marsh Company in Boston had a figure in colonial dress painted on a billboard overlooking their new construction and asked me to make a miniature sculpture of it. This figure was sold in their stores and we made several thousand of them."

SML 93 Democratic Victory *1948/800*

"1948 was an election year and we made a figure of a politically minded donkey sitting on an elephant as an indication of his party's victory."

Not available for photography

SML 94 Republican Victory *1948/800*

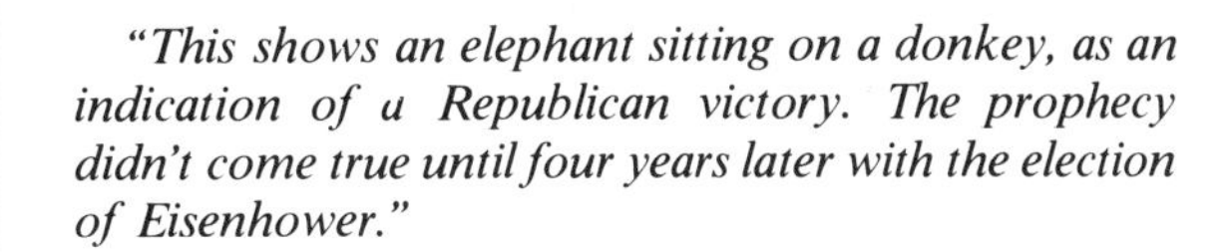

"This shows an elephant sitting on a donkey, as an indication of a Republican victory. The prophecy didn't come true until four years later with the election of Eisenhower."

SML 95 Mr. Rittenhouse Square *1948/SSR*

"Philadelphia's Mr. Rittenhouse Square wearing a homburg hat and in formal morning dress indicates his background by a variety of containers all filled with scrapple."

SML 96 Mrs. Rittenhouse Square *1948/SSR*

"Mrs. Rittenhouse Square is apparently museum-hopping and is disdainfully gazing through her lorgnette at a bust of Benjamin Franklin."

SML 97 Mr. Sheraton *1948/200*

"Made for the Sheraton Hotel Corporation and shows the gentleman in period dress leaning against a Sheraton bookcase."

SML 98 A Harvey Girl *1948/1,500*

"She is shown in the costume of a waitress in the chain of restaurants on the Atcheson, Topeka and the Santa Fe railroad."

SML 99 Mary Lyon *1948/750*

"She was the founder of Mount Holyoke College. In our figurine she is presented as she appeared raising funds for the school. She always carried a small green cloth bag which we have shown beside her. It was used to carry home the money."

SML 100 James Monroe *1948/SSR*

"James Monroe, sixth president of the United States, is holding the Monroe Doctrine."

SML 101 Elizabeth Monroe *1948/SSR*

"One of the most gracious hostesses of the White House."

SML 102 Spirit of '76 *1948/Open (6213)*

"This is from the painting in Abbot Hall made for the first of two Marblehead tercentenaries." (Prescott Baston's Studio is a block away from Abbot Hall).

SML 103 Nathaniel Hawthorne *1948/SSR*

"Mr. Hawthorne is seated at the desk in the Customs House where he was working during the period when he wrote The Scarlett Letter. *He is seated on a three-legged stool which is described in one of his novels and holds a replica of the account book which is on exhibit at the Customs House and shows his signature."*

SML 104 House of Seven Gables *1948/Open (6121)*

"A miniature of the house in which the action of Hawthorne's story took place. It has been sold for many years in the retail line."

SML 105 House of Seven Gables (Salem Rotary Club) *1948/1,500*

"It has been used by the Salem Rotary Club as a gift for visiting Rotarians."

SML 106 Swedish Girl *1948/SSR*

"A young girl in the costume of the Dalarna section of Sweden."

Not available for photography

SML 107 Swedish Boy *1948/SSR*

"In the costume of the Dalarna section of Sweden."

SML 108 Becky Thatcher *1948/Open (6131)*

"Becky is standing at her desk in a schoolroom, holding behind her back a peach which Tom Sawyer has passed to her. He has written on her slate 'Please take it, I have more'."

SML 109 Tom Sawyer *1948/Open (6132)*

"Tom is standing in front of the fence which he later got his friends to paint for him. He has the bucket of whitewash and a very big brush."

SML 110 Huckleberry Finn *1948/Open (6133)*

"Huck is asleep on a river bank with a fishline in one hand draped between his toes into the river flowing in front of him."

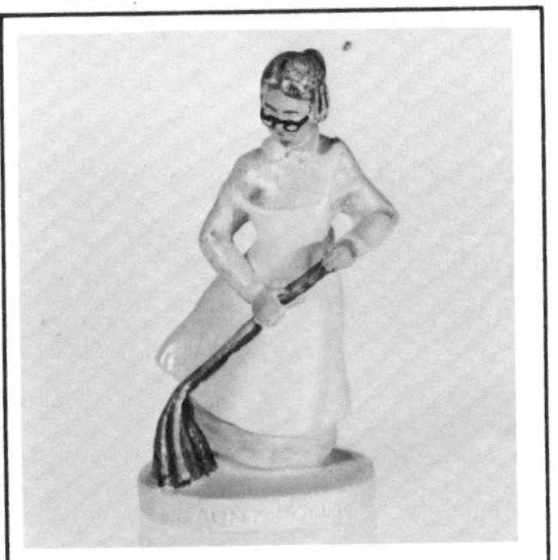

SML 111 Aunt Polly *1948/Open (6135)*

"Tom Sawyer's Aunt Polly is vigorously sweeping her house which was always in need of cleaning because of the exuberance of her nephews."

SML 112 Jim *1948/Open (6136)*

"Jim is the black who floated down the river on a raft with Huckleberry Finn."

SML 113 Babe Ruth *1948/SSR*

"A miniature of the great ballplayer, leaning on his bat, while a member of the New York Yankees. I still think it's a shame the Red Sox let him go."

SML 114 Thomas Jefferson *1949/Open (6003)*

"Third president of the United States, shown as he steps forward with his draft of the Declaration of Independence which he presented to the Colonists gathered in Philadelphia."

SML 115 Oliver Twist and the Parish Beadle *1949 Open (6115)*

"Oliver is holding the cuff of the Beadle's coat as he is being led from the orphanage to his job as an apprentice to an undertaker. He has all of his worldly possessions in a box six inches square and four inches deep."

SML 116 Menotomy Indian *1949/2,500*

"This miniature of a Cyrus Dallin original was made to give to the depositors of the Menotomy Trust Company."

SML 117 Menotomy Indian (Pen Stand) *1949/1,500*

SML 118 Paul Bunyan *1949/Open*

(Discontinued forever on Oct. 31, 1978)

"A miniature of the legendary lumberman straddling a river where two or three small houses can be seen between his feet."

SML 119 Patrick Henry *1949/SSR*

"The noted orator is standing at a podium at which he made his famous statement, 'Give me Liberty, or give me Death'."

SML 120 Sarah Henry *1949/SSR*

"The wife of the orator with a somewhat skeptical attitude, so familiar to the wives of notable public speakers."

SML 121 Gathering Tulips *1949/SSR*

"A girl in Dutch costume with a basket of tulips in her hands."

SML 122 Dutchman's Pipe *1949/SSR*

"A man in Dutch costume sitting in a Dutch splat-backed chair and smoking a long Dutchman's pipe."

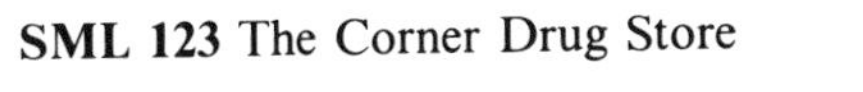

SML 123 The Corner Drug Store *1949/Open*

(6211)

"A chocolate salesman of a hundred years ago displaying his product to a pharmacist in a very elaborate drug store."

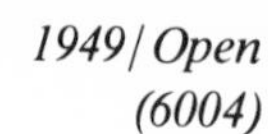

SML 124 Betsy Ross *1949/Open (6004)*

"Betsy is showing the newly completed Stars and Stripes with her sewing basket beside her and seated in a Chippendale chair of a design still used in the Betsy Ross house."

SML 125 The Clown *1949/Open*
(Discontinued forever on Oct. 31, 1979)

"This miniature shows Emmett Kelly, the famous clown, in the middle of his act which involves cleaning up after the procession of elephants."

SML 126 Giant Royal Bengal Tiger *1949/SSR*

"The tiger is shown on a pedestal and performing at the command of the tamer in the Ringling Brothers Circus."

SML 127 Boy Scout (Plaque) *1949/2,500*

"The Statue of Liberty is the background for a kneeling Boy Scout who is holding a shield depicting the Stars and Stripes."

Not available for
photography

SML 128 Uncle Mistletoe (Marshall Field) *1949/ 1,500*

"I designed this for Marshall Field. He is the Chicago store's Christmas trademark."

SML 129 Santa Claus *1949/Open (6222)*

"This piece was originally made for the R. H. Macy Company in New York City at the time the movie 'The Miracle on 34th Street' was being shown. A little girl is sitting on Santa's knee, a meeting which is supposed to have healed the breach between Macy's and Gimbel's."

SML 130 Yankee Sea Captain *1949/Open (6241)*

"This young man is standing at the gangway of his Clipper Ship. He is supervising the stowing of cargo prior to his departure to China."

SML 131 The Thinker (*Le Penseur*) *1949/SSR*

"The sculptor of the full-sized figure is Auguste Rodin. This is taken from the bronze in the Metropolitan Museum."

SML 132 The Thinker (Pen Stand) *1949/SSR*

SML 133 The Mark Twain Home in Hannibal, Missouri *1949/SSR*

"This shows the house in Hannibal, Missouri, which furnished the fence for Tom Sawyer's painting experience."

SML 134 Mary Had a Little Lamb *1949/Open (6403)*

"Mary and her lamb are approaching her teacher in front of the schoolhouse."

SML 135 The Cow Jumped Over The Moon *1949/Open (6402)*

"The cow is just descending from her flight over the moon. The dish is still running, the cat still fiddling, and the dog still laughing."

SML 136 Jack and Jill *1949/Open (6401)*

"Jack and Jill are going up a steep flight of stairs with an empty pail and Jack wearing a high silk hat. On the other side, they have tumbled down and the crown of Jack's hat is broken."

SML 137 Eustace Tilley, Esq. *1949/500*

"Mr. Tilley is the legendary character who graces the cover of The New Yorker *magazine every year on the anniversary of its founding. The magazine used the miniature in a promotion."*

SML 138 John Hancock *1949/12,000*

"This figurine was sold for many years to the John Hancock Mutual Life Insurance Company. It is a miniature in full color of the four-foot bronze in the lobby of the John Hancock building."

SML 139 John Hancock (Pen Stand) *1949/3,000*

SML 140 Ichabod Crane *1949/SSR*

"Ichabod, the school teacher from the big city, is demonstrating an intricate dance step while ogling Katrina Van Tassel."

SML 141 Katrina Van Tassel *1949/SSR*

"Katrina is dancing in response to the teachings of Mr. Crane, thereby infuriating Brom Bones."

SML 142 Brom Bones (The Headless Horseman) *1949/SSR*

"Brom is the sturdy country suitor of Katrina. Annoyed at the incursion of Mr. Crane, Brom saddles his horse. Pretending to be a legendary decapitated Hessian horseman, he throws the pumpkin carried in his arms at the dismayed Ichabod and scares him out of town."

SML 143 Diedrich Knickerbocker *1950/SSR*

"The nom de plume *of Washington Irving. Shown here as an irascible Dutchman, surging out of his study with a wake of books and documents trying to quiet the children of the household."*

SML 144 Dame Van Winkle *1950/SSR*

"Dame Van Winkle has her mouth widely opened as she indignantly yells at her lazy husband. She has a cast-iron frying pan in her hand and has every intention of giving him a clout with it."

SML 145 Rip Van Winkle *1950/SSR*

"Some 20 years after leaving home he plods his way homeward with what is left of his once splendid gun at his side."

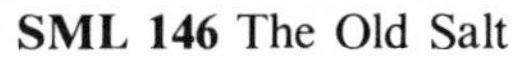
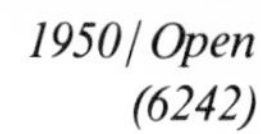

SML 146 The Old Salt *1950/Open (6242)*

"A New England coastal character, dressed in oilskins, is shown mending a net."

SML 147 Spirit of '76 (Paperweight) *1950/SSR*
(See SML 102).

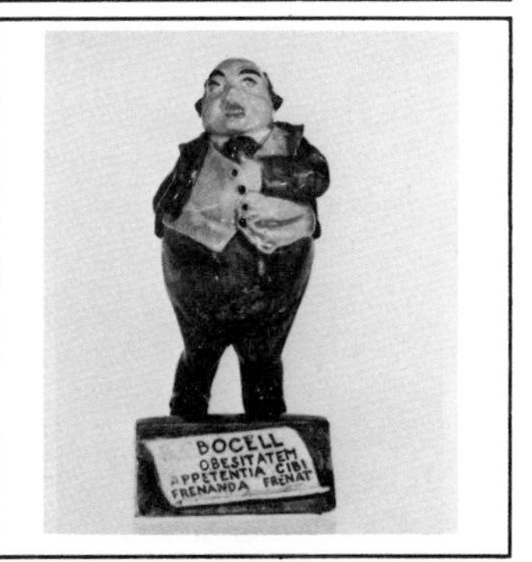

SML 148 Obocell *1950/45,000*

"This figure was made for a patent medicine firm which sold a remedy for obesity based on the theory of cutting down the patient's appetite. Mr. Obocell has become so bloated that in bending over, the seat of his trousers has ripped and he has just discovered the damage."

SML 149 Tom Bowline, Ashore *1950/Open (6246)*

"Tom Bowline, the generic term for a common sailor, is returning from a long voyage with a duffle bag over his shoulder and a parrot in a cage in the other hand. His costume is authentic and derived from exhibits at the Peabody Museum in Salem."

Not available for photography

SML 150 Tom Bowline (Pen Stand) *1950/SSR*

SML 151 The Cow Hand *1950/Open (6508)*

"This cowboy is surrounded by sagebrush. He is wearing a six-shooter and carrying the ever-present lariat."

SML 152 Malvolio *1950/SSR*

"The butler in the home of Countess Olivia. He has been deceived by a letter telling him that the Countess is in love with him and that he is to smile continuously, wear cross garters and yellow, the color she abhors."

SML 153 Countess Olivia *1950/SSR*

"An aristocratic young lady is startled at the aberrations of her employee but is reassured when her cousin admits to having conned the poor fellow into his erratic behavior."

SML 154 Mark Antony *1950/SSR*

"The proud Roman commander is standing beside his chariot while he gazes imperiously around the Egyptian city."

SML 155 Cleopatra *1950/SSR*

"The Queen of the Egyptians is leaning gracefully against a sphinx statue which is engraved with several hieroglyphs."

SML 156 Touchstone, the Jester *1950/SSR*

"Touchstone in his multi-colored costume is seated by the side of a road, cynically sizing up the local citizens. His attention is attracted by Audrey."

SML 157 Audrey, a Country Wench *1950/SSR*

"She is passing down the lane leading her goat to pasture and draws the attention of Touchstone."

SML 158 Paul Revere *1950/Open (6243)*

"The silversmith of Boston made famous by his service rendered to the Colonial plotters for independence, frequently the messenger of the Revolutionary development. In this case, he is spreading the alarm to Lexington and Concord."

SML 159 The Town Crier *1950/Open (6247)*

"The Town Crier was the indispensible purveyor of communications in the colonial communities. He kept the people informed, with his brass bell and leather lungs."

SML 160 Mother and Baby (National Diaper Service) *1950/2,000*

"This mother of the '50's, shown changing her baby on a bathinette, was sold to the Diaper Service Institute and was used for advertising and public relations."

SML 161 The Swan Boat *1950/Open (6244)*

"A very limited excursion boat which makes a tour around the pond in the Public Gardens in Boston. My son is on the front bench wearing a captain's hat. The mallard ducks from Make Way For the Ducklings *are catching peanuts alongside the boat."*

SML 162 Andrew Jackson *1950/Open (6011)*

"The seventh president of the United States is shown in the uniform he wore when commanding at the Battle of New Orleans, which was the conclusion of the War of 1812."

SML 163 Phoebe *1950/SSR*

"The heroine of The House of Seven Gables. *She rescues her elderly relatives from their confusion and poverty and lifts a curse from the family."*

SML 164 Donald McKay *1950/Open (6249)*

"Shown in his shipyard displaying the half-model of his first Yankee Clipper, Staghound. *The ship model is mounted on an elaborate billethead. Mr. McKay is persuading the bankers and financiers that a slender, fast ship will earn more money than a pot-bellied slow packet."*

SML 165 Will Rogers *1950/Open (6012)*

"The Western philosopher is holding his lariat, pulling his ear, and giving out with wisecracking wisdom."

SML 166 Motif No. 1 *1950/Open (6245)*

"The fish house in Rockport, Massachusetts, reputed to have been the source material for more paintings than any other building in the country. Shown as it appeared before its destruction in the East coast snowstorm of February, 1978. It has since been reconstructed and the original charm has been maintained."

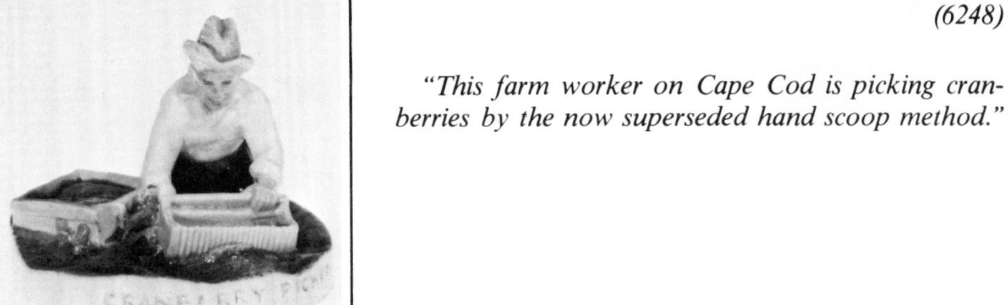

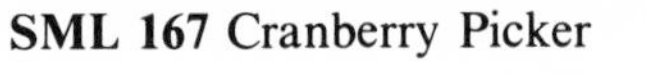

SML 167 Cranberry Picker *1950/Open (6248)*

"This farm worker on Cape Cod is picking cranberries by the now superseded hand scoop method."

SML 168 Chiquita Banana *1951/2,000*

"This is the trademark of the United Fruit Company and was made for sale on their 'Great White Fleet' and to be used in general corporate promotion."

SML 169 A second version of Chiquita Banana with a palm tree *1951/1,500*

SML 170 Chiquita Banana (Ash Tray) *1951/1,500*

SML 171 Francis Drake *1951/SSR*

"This is a miniature of a figurehead in the Marine Museum in Mystic, Connecticut."

SML 172 Jackie Gleason *1951/200*

"The same as the Francis Drake miniature but with Jackie Gleason's head. I redesigned this for a special Gleason appearance in Boston."

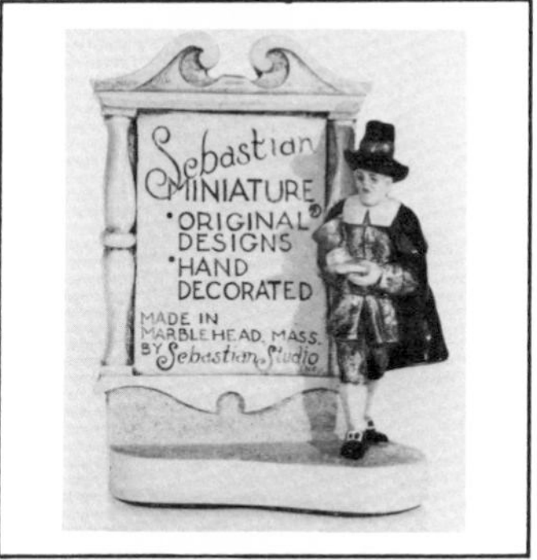

SML 173 Sebastian Plaque *1951/SSR*
(Discontinued forever on Dec. 31, 1978)

"Made for a counter display. It is a colonial sign with our Town Crier figurine beside it."

SML 174 Madonna of Chair *1951/Open*
(6311)

"A miniature sculpture derived from Raphael's painting."

SML 175 The Penny Shop *1951/Open (6122)*

"Hepzibah Pyncheon of the House of Seven Gables *is at the counter of her Penny Shop selling gingerbread to a neighborhood boy."*

SML 176 Jessie Buffam (Down East) *1951/SSR*

"An announcer at Radio Station WEEI. The miniature was made for publicity purposes. Sold a couple of thousand and then put it into the line as 'Down East'."

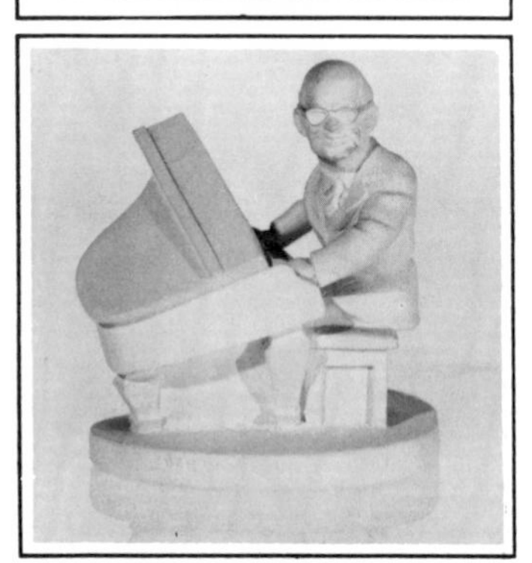

SML 177 Carl Moore (The Piano Player) *1951/ Open (6509)*

"An announcer at Radio Station WEEI. Also made for publicity purposes. Sold a couple of thousand and then put it into the line as 'The Piano Player'."

SML 178 Caroline Cabot *1951/1,500*

"Same as above, another WEEI personality, but this figurine was not put into the line."

SML 179 Mother Parker *1951/1,500*

"Same as above but not put into the line. She was a cooking editor and is tossing a salad."

Not available for photography

SML 180 Charles Ashley *1951/1,500*

"Was a WEEI News Editor. I showed him reading from a long teletype script."

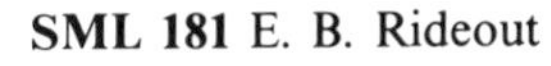

SML 181 E. B. Rideout *1951/1,500*

"E. B. was the weather announcer at WEEI and is pointing out a temperature of 120 degrees. He has also brought his weathervane into the studio."

SML 182 Priscilla Fortescue *1951/1,500*

"Fashion announcer for WEEI. Because of her enthusiasm for horses and camping, she is modeled in a riding habit, standing in front of a log cabin and being gazed at admiringly by her horse."

SML 183 The Lacemaker *1951/Open (6301)*

"A young mother in a ladderback chair, rocking a cradle with one foot and busily occupied with the bobbins that create a pillow-lace design."

SML 184 Lacemaker (Pen Stand) *1951/SSR*

"The same as above but as a pen stand."

SML 185 Lacemaker (Pen Stand) *1951/500*

"I made this for the Gem Crib and Cradle Co."

SML 186 Baby Buggy of 1850 *1951/Open (6303)*

"A young mother with her child in an antique perambulator."

SML 187 The Weaver *1951/Open (6302)*

"A young mother at a loom is being imitated by her son seated in a box which he conceives to be a loom."

SML 188 The Observer and Dame Boston (Jordan Marsh) *1951/2,000*

"The Jordan Marsh Observer (See SML 92) has left his position at the fence and is escorting Dame Boston around the premises."

Not available for photography

SML 189 The Old Man of the Mountain *1951/SSR*

"A naturalistic version of New Hampshire's 'Great Stone Face'."

SML 190 College Seal (MIT) *1951/300*

"College Seal for Massachusetts Institute of Technology, Class of 1916."

SML 191 College Seal (MIT) *1951/500*

"Same as above, Class of 1952."

SML 192 Observer on Horseback (Jordan Marsh) *1951/3,000*

"The Observer is now on horseback, as per the advertising slogan: 'The Allied White Horses'."

SML 193 The Iron Master's House *1951/SSR*

"The home of the superintendent of the Saugus Iron Works, built about 1635."

SML 194 Christopher Columbus *1951/SSR*

"Columbus is standing beside a lantern on the Santa Maria.*"*

SML 195 The Madonna of the Goldfinch *1951/ Open (6312)*

"This is from the Raphael painting and shows the Madonna with Jesus. John the Baptist pets a goldfinch."

SML 196 Judge Pyncheon *1951/SSR*

"The villain of The House of Seven Gables *is marching relentlessly toward the house which he intends to seize."*

SML 197 Chief Pontiac *1951/250*

"A bust of an Indian chief with a three-feather headdress and bear-claw necklace. I made this for a special promotion."

SML 198 Sistine Madonna *1951/Open (6313)*

"This is the third (SML 174 and 195) and last of Raphael's Madonnas."

SML 199 Scottish Girl (Jello) *1952/3,000*

"This is a girl in Scottish costume looking at her budget book. She has come to the conclusion that 'Now's the Time for Jello'."

SML 200 Lost in the Kitchen (Jello) *1952/3,000*

"A fat man, surrounded by cooking utensils and wearing his wife's apron, is in dismay at the prospect of preparing a meal. 'Now's the Time for Jello'."

SML 201 Benjamin Franklin *1952/Open (6006)*

"The statesman and philosopher is returning from his kite-flying episode carrying the kite and speculating on the implications of his venture."

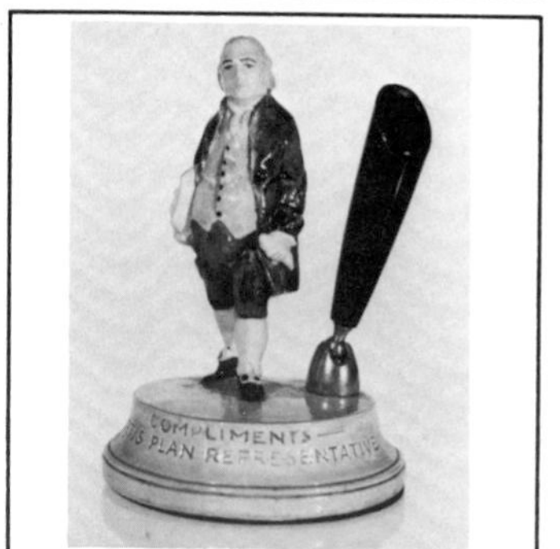

SML 202 Ben Franklin (Pen Stand) *1952/1,800*

"Used by the Curtis Publishing Co."

SML 203 Ben Franklin (Paperweight) *1952/2,500*

"Used by Keystone Reader's Service (also Curtis Publishing, Saturday Evening Post*)."*

SML 204 Tabasco Sauce *1952/1,000*
"Wake Up Food Flavors"

"There is a small bottle of tabasco sauce on one side of this piece and its effects are illustrated by a man in Spanish costume taking his siesta. Behind him the same man, having had a taste of tabasco, is about to break into a delighted dance."

SML 205 The Fat Man (Jello) *1952/5,000*

"A man, just out of the shower, is standing on the bathroom scale and has come to the obvious conclusion that 'Now's the Time for Jello'."

SML 206 Baby (Jello) *1952/3,000*

"A young man with one tooth is throwing his breakfast dishes right and left and yelling at the top of his voice 'Now's the Time for Jello'."

SML 207 Aerial Tramway, Franconia, NH *1952/1,500*

"A model of the tower and base station of the tramway with one of the cars parked at the summit."

SML 208 Aerial Tramway (Second Version) *1952/1,000*

"One of the towers with ascending and descending cars parked."

SML 209 The Favored Scholar *1952/SSR*

"A miniature of the 30-inch sculptural group by John Rogers. It shows a young man teacher at a high desk explaining some course of study to an attractive young lady student, while a youthful male student tries to break up the conversation."

SML 210 Neighboring Pews *1952/SSR*

"A miniature of the sculptural group by John Rogers. A young gentleman is leaning over the pew in front of him to show an attractive young lady the hymn number. He is inadvertently jostling a somewhat less attractive elderly lady in the process."

SML 211 Weighing the Baby *1952/SSR*

"A miniature of the sculptural group by John Rogers. A young mother has brought her baby to the grocery store to be weighed. She and the grocer are astonished at the baby's progress. However, the baby's brother is pulling a corner of the blanket increasing the weight by several pounds."

SML 212 Marblehead Plantation *1952/1,000*

"This is a plaque with the seal of the Town of Marblehead. I made it for the Marblehead high school."

SML 213 The First House, Plymouth Plantation *1952/SSR*

"This is a miniature of the prototype house built by the earliest New England settlers."

SML 214 Charles Dickens *1952/Open (6117)*

"This miniature shows Emlyn Williams recreating the appearances of Charles Dickens, reading from his own works. The figurine was originally sold to the Sol Hurok organization which used it as a gift to drama critics in the cities where Williams was scheduled to appear. We sold several hundred of the figurines and then put it into our retail line."

SML 215 Colonial Kitchen *1952/Open (6251)*

"This is the fireplace from the ironmaster's house (See SML 189) and shows the housewife preparing dinner in the vast fireplace with one of her children seated beside the fire."

SML 216 Saint Joan of Arc *1952/SSR*

"Made for Bishop Wright of Worcester, Massachusetts, who had a special interest in Joan of Arc and distributed it to the people of his diocese. It was later put into the retail line."

SML 217 Saint Sebastian *1952/SSR*

"Made for the St. Sebastian School in Newton, Massachusetts. It was used by them as an award and fund-raiser and later placed in the retail line."

SML 218 Stork (Jello) *1952/3,000*

"The stork is flying through some fluffy clouds with a pink blanket hooked over his beak and a complete set of triplets in the blanket. 'Now's the Time for Jello'."

SML 219 Our Lady of Good Voyage *1952/SSR*

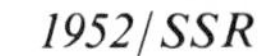

"This was made for the Portuguese Roman Catholic Church of Gloucester and was carried in their fishing vessels by many members of the local fleet. It was later put into the retail line."

SML 220 Ride to the Hounds *1953/Open (6234)*

"This is a Victorian child derived from Godey's Ladies Book *of the 1850's. The boy is vigorously galloping on his rocking horse."*

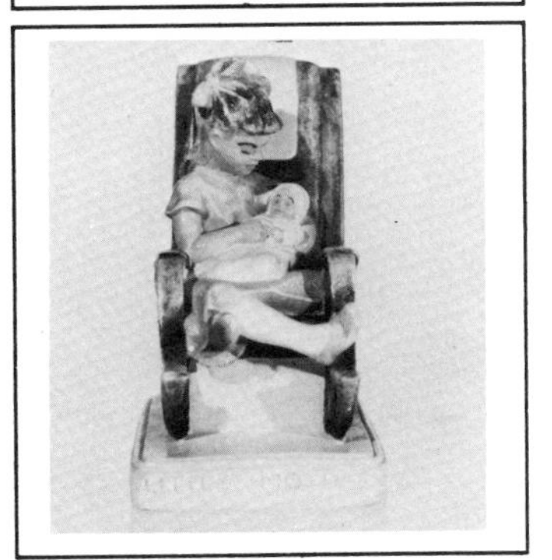

SML 221 Little Mother *1953/Open (6231)*

"Another Godey child. Seated at a period rocking chair with her favorite doll."

SML 222 Switching the Freight *1953/Open (6236)*

"Another Godey child. This boy is semi-reclining on the floor while propelling his toy train. I used my son as the model."

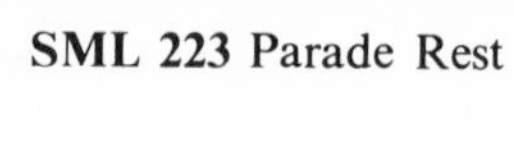

SML 223 Parade Rest *1953/Open (6233)*

"Another Godey child. This boy is in the Civil War uniform of a Zouave and has been briskly beating on his drum. He has just stopped in answer to a parental request."

SML 224 Games in Springtime *1953/Open (6232)*

"Another Godey child. The young lady has been rolling her hoop and has just stopped while she considers the next hill."

SML 225 Speak for It *1953/Open (6235)*

"The final Godey child in this 1953 series. The young lady is holding a tempting morsel before her dog as she wants him to speak for it."

SML 226 The Boy Christ of Nazareth *1953/500*

"For the Children's Home of Nazareth in Massachusetts. It shows Jesus as a boy in the temple talking with the elders."

Not available for photography

SML 227 Julie Billiart *1953/300*

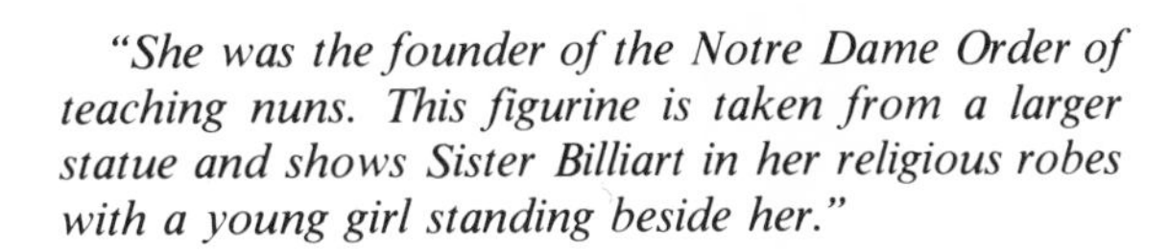

"She was the founder of the Notre Dame Order of teaching nuns. This figurine is taken from a larger statue and shows Sister Billiart in her religious robes with a young girl standing beside her."

SML 228 Pioneer Village *1953/Open (6252)*

"Shows an early colonial building with two men, one in stocks and the other in a pillory."

SML 229 Holgrave, the Daguerreotypist *1953/SSR*

"This character from The House of Seven Gables *was a professional photographer when the equipment was very elementary and bulky."*

SML 230 "Old Put" Enjoys A Licking at Bunker Hill *1953/200*

"The Putnam Pantry Candies Company, run by direct descendants of General Israel Putnam, requested a version of their ancestor for advertising and retail sales. General Putnam is depicted leaning against the Bunker Hill monument and licking out the inside of a chocolate kettle."

SML 231 The School Boy of 1850 *1953/150*

"This is a miniature of a statue near the campus of Cushing Academy in Ashburnham, Massachusetts. It was made for the town Service Committee who wished to raise funds to help their local servicemen during the Korean War."

SML 232 St. Teresa of Lisieux *1953/SSR*

"Made for our retail line at a suggestion of the Carmelite religious order. It was sold for a number of years."

SML 233 Boy and Pelican (The Fishermen) *1953/ Open (6228)*

"A young man is sitting on the piles of a Florida harbor, fishing. A pelican is behind him manifesting a considerable interest in the young man's catch."

SML 234 Old Powder House-1775 *1953/SSR*

"This Powder House in a suburb of Boston contained the store of powder used to force the British fleet from Boston Harbor."

SML 238 The Bluebird Girl *1954/1,500*

"Made for the Campfire Girls of America, it shows a member of the youngest group patting a huge inflated bluebird."

SML 237 The Old Covered Bridge *1954/Open (6253)*

"A buggy is just emerging from our model of a covered bridge which spans two abutments of a placid river."

SML 236 Whale (Jello) *1954/2,000*

"The whale is coasting happily in the surf anticipating 'A Whale of a Dessert!'"

SML 235 Lion (Jello) *1953/3,000*

"The lion with his widely opened jaws is anticipating that 'Now's the Time for Jello'."

SML 239 Campfire Girl *1954/2,500*

"Made for the Campfire Girls of America, she is standing beside an outdoor fireplace which has the Campfire emblem on it."

SML 240 Horizon Girl *1954/1,000*

"Made for Campfire Girls of America, It shows an adult member of the organization ready to follow the Campfire teachings in her adult life."

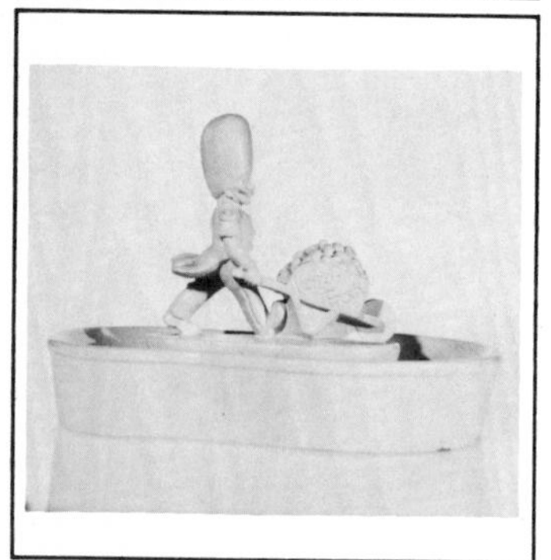

SML 241 Kernel-Fresh *1954/1,500*

"This was made for a packaged nuts company. It shows a man in the uniform of the Grenadier Guards with a wheelbarrow load of mixed nuts. His name is Kernel-Fresh."

SML 242 Rabbit (Jello) *1954/3,000*

"An elegant rabbit is giving away his salad."

SML 243 William Penn *1954/2,000*

"Made for the Penn Mutual Life Insurance Company, this is a miniature of the bronze statue in Philadelphia. It was sold to the insurance company but was distributed exclusively by the president as it was visible from his office."

SML 244 St. Pius (Pope Pius X) *1954/1,400*

"Made for the Archdiocese of Boston, it is a miniature of the statue in the Holy Cross Cathedral."

SML 245 Yankee Clipper Ship *1954/Open (6254)*

"This model of a squarerigger under full sail was made for an insurance company. When their program was finished, the model was placed in the retail line."

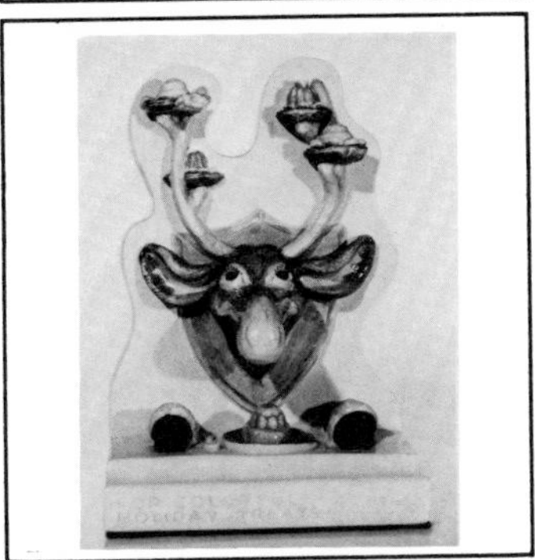

SML 246 Reindeer (Jello) *1954/2,000*

"This piece features a trophy of a reindeer head about to consume a dish of Jello with several subsequent dishes perched in his antlers."

SML 247 Dachshund (Audiovox) *1954/500*

"Made for the Audiovox Corporation. Because the animal is cocking his head, Audiovox (who made hearing aids) thought it was an appropriate symbol for their advertising."

SML 248 The Nativity *1954/Open (6314)*

"This piece is the traditional Nativity grouping. With the Madonna and Child in the center, Joseph and animals beside her, shepherds coming in from one side and the Wisemen and the camels from the other."

SML 249 Our Lady of La Leche *1954/SSR*

"Replica of a statue venerated at the Mission of Nombre de Dios, St. Augustine, Florida."

SML 250 The Doctor *1954/Open (6214)*

"This model is derived from the painting by Sir Luke Fildes who was court painter for Queen Victoria. The figure has been in our retail line for many years and has been produced as a pen stand and pen-stand paperweight. In the last form we sold 10,000 to one patent medicine firm."

SML 251 The Doctor (Pen Stand) *1954/SSR*

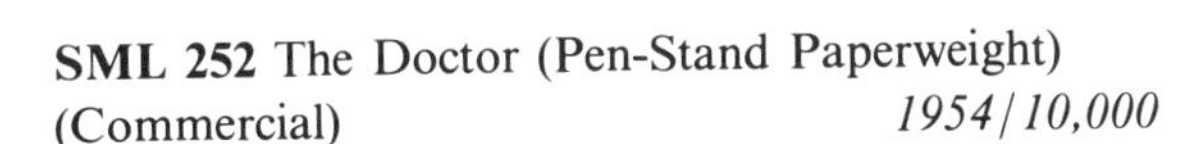

SML 252 The Doctor (Pen-Stand Paperweight) (Commercial) *1954/10,000*

SML 253 Swan Boat—Empty Seats (Brooch) *1954/500*

"This version with empty benches was made for a WBZ television station promotion."

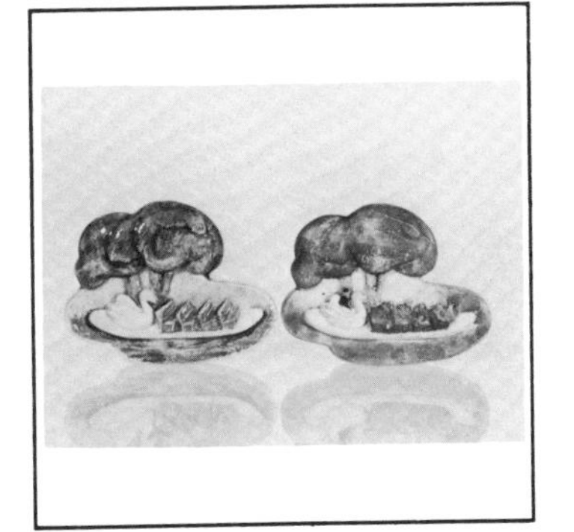

SML 254 Swan Boat—Full Seats (Brooch) *1954/500*

"This version has people on the benches."

SML 255 Scuba Diver *1954/SSR*

"This is a model showing many forms of undersea vegetation and a young man in scuba diving costume."

SML 256 Giraffe (Jello) *1955/2,500*

"A giraffe is appreciating the serving of Jello which he finds in the upper branches of an African tree. 'Everyone Reaches for Jello'."

SML 257 Captain Doliber *1955/SSR*

"This Marblehead captain is at the wheel of a remodeled America's Cup defender. The vessel had been bought by a Marblehead yachtsman and was used by his family for several years."

SML 258 Second Bank/State Street Trust Company (Pen Stand) *1955/200*

"This piece was made after the Second Bank and the State Street Trust were combined. It shows the old State House, a symbol of one of the banks, superimposed on a large figure 2."

SML 259 Old Woman in the Shoe (Jello) *1955/3,500*

"Kids Love Jello."

SML 260 Horse Head (Pen Stand) *1955/SSR*

"In our retail line. An occasional person from a horse show committee bought it for a trophy."

SML 261 Santa (Jello) *1955/4,000*

"Santa Claus has just come down the chimney and finds a large serving of Jello waiting for him. The boy who has prepared it is asleep under the table."

SML 262 Dachshund *1955/SSR*

"This was prepared for local dachshund breeders and follows their standard lines."

SML 263 Eastern Paper Manufacturers *1956/200*

"A Three-dimensional version of their trademark."

SML 264 Royal Bengal Lancer *1956/100*

"Made for a TV program sponsored by General Foods."

SML 265 Robin Hood and Friar Tuck *1956/500*

"For Johnson & Johnson. Friar Tuck carries Robin Hood over the stream."

SML 266 Robin Hood and Little John *1956/500*

"For Johnson & Johnson. The struggle on the bridge."

SML 267 Robin Hood and Little John *1956/*
(Prototype)

"Little John has won the struggle on the bridge. The figure was never used."

SML 268 Three Little Kittens (Jello) *1956/3500*

"Mother Dear, See Here, See Here."

SML 269 Texcel Tape *1956/2,000*

"For Johnson & Johnson. A schoolboy advertising Texcel Tape."

SML 270 The Tower of Tape *1956/2,000*

"For Permacel Tape. They wanted to show all the types of tape they made."

SML 271 Elsie the Cow *1956/1,000*

Shows Elsie the Cow with a billboard on which various messages could be placed."

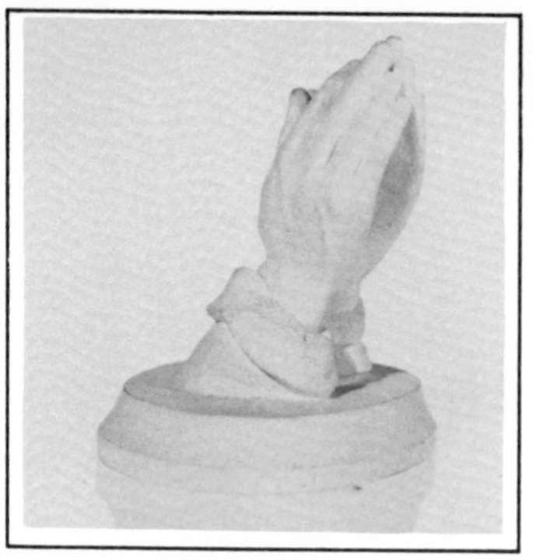

SML 272 Praying Hands *1956/SSR*

"From the drawing by Albrecht Durer."

SML 273 Blacksmith (Johnson & Johnson)
1956/1,500

"Made for the Ortho Branch of Johnson & Johnson, a blacksmith plugs Rarical Tablets. This model later became our retail blacksmith."

SML 274 Girl on Diving Board *1956/300*

"Made for a Brooklyn Hotel that advertised 'the largest swimming pool'."

SML 275 Mrs. Obocell *1956/2,000*

"Made as a companion piece for Mr. Obocell."

SML 276 New York University Graduate School of Business Administration building. *1956/700*

"We made seven hundred of them for fund raising."

SML 277 Arthritic Hands (Johnson & Johnson) *1956/400*

Johnson & Johnson asked me to sculpt a pair of hands for use with the promotion of a drug that eased the pain of arthritis. I used the Durer model."

SML 278 Nurse (Mead-Johnson) *1956/800*

"Shows a nurse with a pair of twins, one sleeping and one lively. I made this for Mead-Johnson and then put it in the retail line."

SML 279 The Jolly Green Giant *1956/5,000*

"I made him as a promotional piece for the Green Giant Company. He's holding an ear of corn and a pod of peas."

SML 280 Michigan Millers Insurance Co. (Pen Stand) *1956/400*

"An antique mill with an overshot wheel, used as the company's trademark."

SML 281 Sylvania Electric Display Stand *1957/1,000*

"This was for Sylvania Electric. They wanted a display stand for electric lamps."

SML 282 The Mayflower (Pen Stand) *1957/SSR*

"I designed this to commemorate the arrival of the Mayflower reproduction, built in England and sailed here in 1957."

SML 283 Speedy Alka Seltzer *1957/2,500*

"I designed Speedy as a promotional figurine for Alka Seltzer."

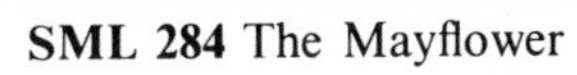

SML 284 The Mayflower *1957/Open (6255)*

"I took this from the pen stand (SML 282)."

SML 285 The Jamestown Church *1957/SSR*

Not available for photography

"The ruins of the old stone church in Jamestown, Virginia. It was in the retail line."

SML 286 Model 305 RAMAC *1957/800*

"I designed this for IBM. It's a scale model of their computer. They used it for advertising."

SML 287 The Glassblower (Pen Stand) *1957/1,200*

"The model of a colonial craftsman producing the early wares of the colony. Used as a commemorative piece by the American Glass Industry."

SML 288 The Glassblower *1957/Open (6216)*

"I took the figure off the commemorative pen stand and put it in the retail line."

SML 289 Jamestown (Plaque) *1957/SSR*

"Designed for the 350th anniversary of Jamestown."

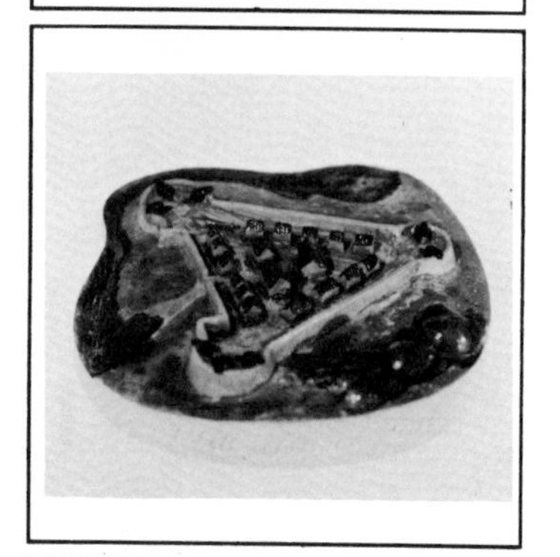

SML 290 The Olde James Fort *1957/SSR*

"A scale model of the original fort at Jamestown. For the 350th anniversary."

SML 291 The Colonial Carriage *1957/Open (6215)*

"Made for the Williamsburg Restoration and sold in the retail line."

SML 292 Colonial Doorway (Pen Stand)
(with penholder missing) *1957/800*

"Made for the Colonial Fund as a pen stand. A Town Crier stands outside the door."

SML 293 The Spoonmen *1957/1,500*

"Made for the National Biscuit Company to advertise Shredded Wheat Juniors."

SML 294 Buffalo Bee *1957/1,500*

"For the National Biscuit Company. A bee in western costume advertises Rice Honeys and Wheat Honeys."

SML 295 The Pilgrims *1958/Open*
(6324)

"The man is carrying a turkey and his wife a basket of vegetables. (From SML 72)."

SML 296 John and Priscilla Alden *1958/Open (6323)*

"Priscilla has her spinning wheel and John his blunderbuss."

SML 297 Victorian Couple *1958/Open (6325)*

"A young couple on a shopping trip."

SML 298 Elsie the Cow (Borden's Centennial) *1957/500*

"Elsie in a party dress."

SML 299 Williamsburg Couple *1958/Open (6322)*

"The Governor and his lady at the Williamsburg Restoration."

SML 300 George and Martha Washington *1958/ Open (6321)*

"Their early days at Mt. Vernon."

SML 301 Mt. Vernon *1958/SSR*

"A scale model of George Washington's home at Mt. Vernon, Va."

Not available for photography

SML 302 Romeo & Juliet *1958/SSR*

"The young lovers together."

SML 303 Salem Savings Bank *1958/500*

"A relief model of their building to commemorate their 140th anniversary."

SML 304 Connecticut Bank and Trust Co. *1958/6,000*

"An allegorical figure indicating cash flow, used for a promotion."

SML 305 Shoemaker (Paperweight) *1958/SSR*

"A Victorian craftsman works at a shoemaker's bench with his tools beside him."

SML 306 Shoemaker (National Bank of Plymouth County) *1958/400*

"Same as above but with a base inscribed National Bank of Plymouth County."

SML 307 Shoemaker (International Shoe Pen stand) *1958/300*

"The Shoemaker as a pen stand for International Shoe Company, St. Louis, MO."

SML 308 Shoemaker (International Shoe-Ewing Pen-stand) *1958/500*

"Pen stand made for International Shoe Co. and presented by Lawrence Ewing."

SML 309 Shoemaker (First County National Bank) *1958/1,000*

SML 310 Shoemaker *1958/Open (6217)*

"I put him on a small base for the bulk of our retail sales."

SML 311 Hannah Duston (Haverhill National Bank Pen Stand) *1958/3,000*

"She is the heroine of Haverhill. She and a teenage boy killed the 11 Indians that had kidnapped her and a group of children."

SML 312 Harvard Colonial Character (Harvard Trust Co.) *1958/4,000*

"I designed as jovial a character as I could."

SML 313 Jordan Marsh Observer (Northshore Shopping Center) *1958/2,500*

"For the new store opening at North Shore. They have given him lobster traps, buoys and a ship's wheels."

SML 314 Jordan Marsh Observer (Northshore Shopping Center) *1958/100*

"This promotion, 'A Better Selling Contest Winner,' tied in to the opening of the Center."

SML 315 The Pioneer Couple *1958/Open (6326)*

"Early settlers in the Midwest."

SML 316 Commodore Stephen Decatur (Decatur National Bank, Decatur, Ill.) *1958/3,000*

"This figure was contracted by letter and telephone and the President of the bank was astonished when I told him my next door neighbor was Stephen Decatur, a direct descendant of the Commodore."

SML 317 Stephen Decatur (Paperweight)
1958/1,000

"The same promotion, bronzed instead of painted."

SML 318 Eskimo (Cliquot Club Ginger Ale Pen Stand) *1958/2,500*

"The Eskimo is holding a bottle of ginger ale."

SML 319 Seated Lincoln (White) *1958/Open (6007)*

"This miniature was made with the collaboration of Mrs. William Penn Cresson, the daughter of Daniel Chester French. It was modeled from French's original sculpture in the Lincoln Memorial."

SML 320 Seated Lincoln (Bronzed) *1958/SSR*

"I prefer the bronzed version, but the white miniature was by far the best seller. I guess people like replicas of what they've seen."

SML 321 Colonial Bell Ringer *1959/Open (6207)*

"A jovial rotund version of the traditional Town Crier."

SML 322 Mrs. S.O.S. *1959/3,000*

"From a cartoon by Hoff and used as premiums for ads in the Reader's Digest. *The model was commissioned by* Reader's Digest *as merchandise rebate to the S.O.S. Company."*

SML 323 Cigar Store Indian (H. P. Hood Co.) *1959/200*

"An exact scale replica of a wooden Indian carving."

SML 324 Weaver (Alexander Smith) *1959/500*

"The Alexander Smith Carpet Company used this subject in their logotype and in 1959 commissioned the Sebastian sculpture. It has been used intermittently since then."

SML 325 Henry Hudson *1959/1,500*

"A figurine of the early explorer of the Hudson River made for the Museum of the City of New York."

SML 326 Giovanni Verazzano *1959/1,500*

"The early Italian explorer, made for the Museum of the City of New York."

SML 327 Fleischman's Margarine (Pen Stand) *1959/2,000*

"Made for Reader's Digest *to be used as a merchandise rebate."*

SML 328 Fleischman's Margarine (Paperweight) *1959/2,000*

(Same use as above.)

SML 329 Alcoa Wrap *1959/1,500*

"The double triangle trademark of the Aluminum Co. of America, given by Reader's Digest *as a merchandise rebate."*

SML 330 Stagecoach (Pen Stand) *1959/500*

"This was made for the Everett National Bank. It is a pen stand and was distributed to their customers. The stagecoach was their trademark because Everett was the Boston terminal of the Newburyport Turnpike over which most of the stage lines traveled."

SML 331 Stagecoach *1959/Open (6258)*

"The same as the preceding but as a figurine for our retail distribution."

SML 332 Fiorello LaGuardia *1959/1,000*

"A caricature of the lovable Mayor of New York. Made for the Museum of the City of New York."

SML 333 The Masonic Bible *1960/250*

"Made for the Philanthropic Lodge A. F. & A. M. of Marblehead on their 200th anniversary."

SML 334 Peter Stuyvestant *1960/1,000*

"For the Museum of the City of New York. This Dutch Governor of New York is shown posed with his usual flair."

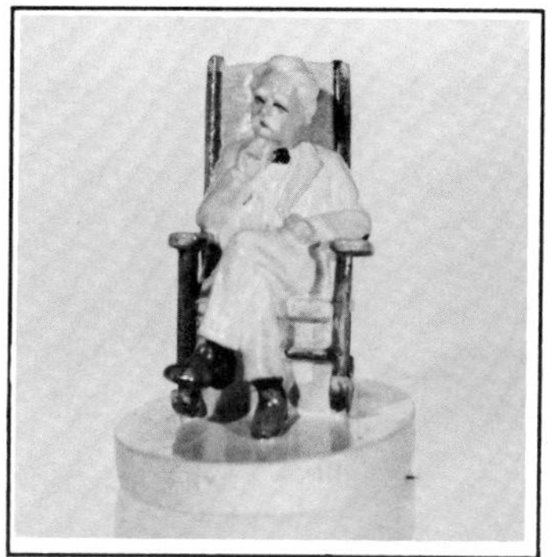

SML 335 Mark Twain *1960/Open (6137)*

"The pose is taken from a series of photographs on the veranda of a friend's home in Peterborough, N.H. He is seated in the usual porch rocking chair."

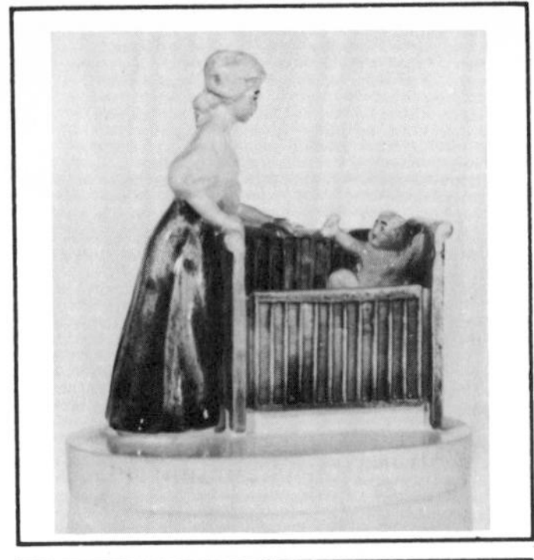

SML 336 Gibson Girl at Home *1960/Open (6304)*

"The Gibson Girl with her long skirt and puffed-sleeve blouse is leaning over the crib where her baby is bouncing."

SML 337 Gibson Girl (Gem Crib and Cradle Co.) *1960/500*

"Same as above, mounted on a base commemorating the Gem Crib and Cradle Company's 50th anniversary."

SML 338 The Shriner *1960/SSR*

"This member of the Ancient Shrine is standing beside his camel."

SML 339 Supp-hose Stocking "Gently Support Your Legs" *1960/1,000*

"Made for Reader's Digest *as a merchandise rebate."*

SML 340 Supp-hose Lady (Pen Stand) *1960/1,500*

"The same model as above, but mounted as a pen stand."

SML 341 Marine Memorial— Hampton Beach, NH *1960/2,500*

"The original was by A. Cosgrove. The miniature was made for public distribution and sale by the State of New Hampshire."

SML 342 Metropolitan Life Tower (Pen Stand) *1960/1,200*

"Made for the Reader's Digest *as a merchandise rebate."*

SML 343 The Infantryman *1960/700*

"Made for Ft. Benning, Georgia. Is a miniature of the heroic statue at Fort Benning. The Infantryman has complete World War II equipment including an M-1 rifle."

SML 344 The Grocery Store *1960/Open (6223)*

"Designed first for a food chain promotion. They didn't use it so I put it in the retail line."

SML 345 Ben Franklin at the Printing Press *1961/Open (6218)*

"Made for The Saturday Evening Post *and later placed in our retail line."*

SML 346 Bunkie Knudsen *1961/150*

"General Motors commissioned this miniature of a man involved in a dealership promotion."

SML 347 Tony Piet *1961/200*

"Second baseman for the Chicago Cubs, this miniature was also made for a General Motors dealership promotion."

SML 348 The Manger *1961/Open*
(6315)

"The central scene of a group depicting the Nativity."

SML 349 The Wisemen *1961/Open*
(6316)

"Designed to accompany the Manger."

SML 350 Shepherds *1961/Open*
(6317)

"Also designed to accompany the Manger."

SML 351 George Washington, Mason *1961/Open*
(6005)

"The only president to be master of a Masonic Lodge and President of the U.S. at the same time."

SML 352 St. Jude Thaddeus *1961/300*

"Made for St. Jude's Church in Chicago."

SML 353 Pope John XXIII *1961/1,500*

"The popular Pope is seated on an elaborate throne in his striking red and white papal robes. Made for the Catholic newspaper in Chicago."

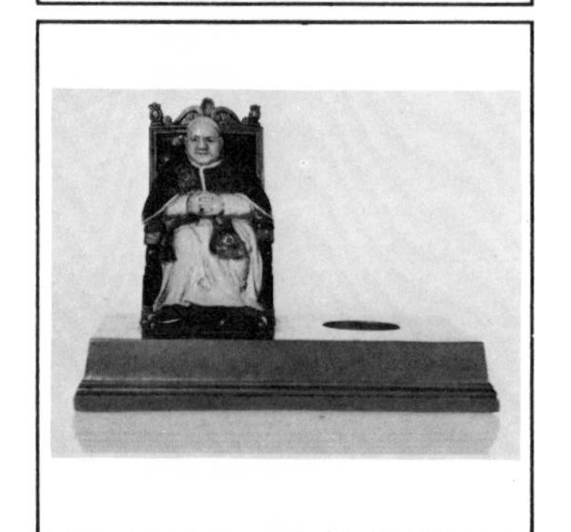

SML 354 Pope John XXIII (Pen Stand) *1961/500*

SML 355 Savin' Sandy *1961/SSR*

"Made for Brown's Department Store in Gloucester, MA. The Scot expresses incredulity that prices could be so low. Later put in our retail line."

SML 356 Savin' Sandy (McNeil Laboratories)
1961/300

"The same figure as above but with the McNeil tartan and sold to McNeil Laboratories, Inc."

SML 357 Merchants Warren National Bank
1961/500

"A bust of young sea captain. This head is typical of the founders of the bank in 1811. The piece commemorated the Bank's 150th anniversary."

SML 358 Seamen's Bank for Savings *1962/1,000*

"This is a relief model of the trademark of the Seamen's Bank showing an Indian who has brought his furs to market and a seaman who uses the bank as a source of capital."

SML 359 Cleopatra *1962/SSR*

"A new model of Cleopatra with a changed head-dress."

SML 360 Big Brother Bob Emery *1962/25*

"This piece was made for the 65th birthday of Bob Emery, a very popular entertainer at radio station WBZ.

SML 361 The Blue Bell Highlander *1962/SSR*

"A figurine of a Scottish girl playing the bagpipes."

Not available for photography

SML 362 Naumkeag Indian *1963/1,000*

"An Indian head used as the trademark of the Naumkeag Trust Company, Salem."

SML 363 Naumkeag Indian *1963/500*

"The same as the above with a bronzed finish."

SML 364 John F. Kennedy *1963/Open (6008)*

"The President, sitting in a rocking chair holding a newspaper."

SML 365 Dia-Mel Fat Man *1963/800*

"A fat man dismayed at the message from his bathroom scale. Made for Dia-Mel, a diet control food."

SML 366 John F. Kennedy Model for a Toby Jug *1963/25*

"This was never used. The President was assassinated a month after I completed the model."

SML 367 Jackie Kennedy Toby Jug *1963/25*

"Also never used."

SML 368 Eskimo *1964/SSR*

"I designed this fellow holding a large fish."

SML 369 New England Home for Little Wanderers *1965/300*

"A brother and sister, given shelter by the New England Home, have been dressed in clean clothing and given a doll and a panda bear. This was sold only to the New England Home."

SML 370 Henry Wadsworth Longfellow *1965/SSR*

"This is a miniature of the bronze in Portland, Maine."

SML 371 Globe (State Street Bank & Trust Company) *1965/400*

"A decorative treatment of the globe with a stand which included a Fahrenheit-Celsius thermometer."

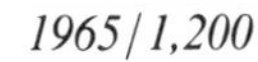

SML 372 Globe *1965/1,200*

"Same as above, without the thermometer."

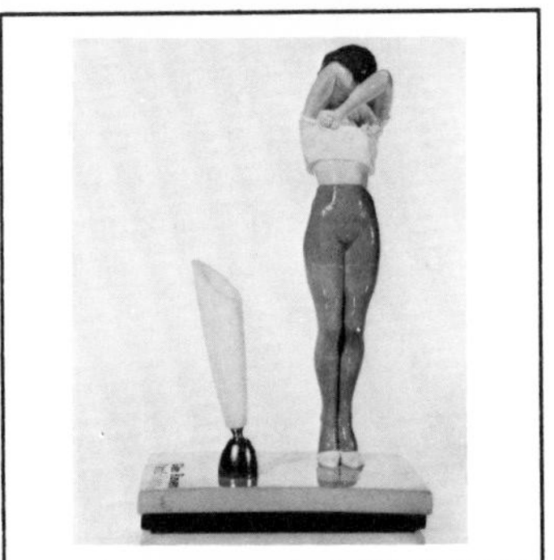

SML 373 Panti-Legs Girl (Pen Stand) *1965/400*

"A sculptural version of the decorative design on Glen Raven's packing box."

SML 374 Baby Music Box (Stanley Home Products) *1965/20,000*

"I designed this as a gift for Stanley Home Products. The miniature rotates on a music box stand."

SML 375 New England Society for the Prevention of Cruelty to Animals *1966/2,000*

"For their Centennial (1868-1968)."

SML 376 Gardeners (Thermometer) *1966/SSR*

"My stores always asked for a miniature that was functional."

SML 377 The Skipper *1966/Open (6256)*

"The skipper is a Marblehead captain at the wheel of a large yacht." (Taken from Captain Doliber-SML 257).

SML 378 Little George *1966/2,500*

"This was made for a bank in Tennessee."

SML 379 Indian (Towne Lyne House) *1966/500*

"The bust of an Indian, used as a trademark."

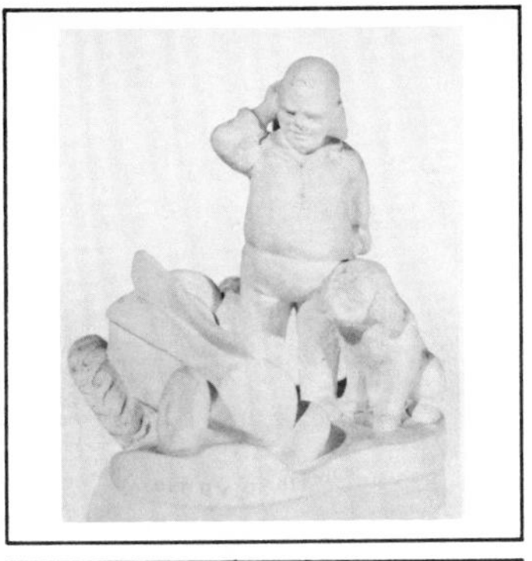

SML 380 Doc Berry of Berwick *1967/150*

"Dr. Berry is shown puzzling how he and his young friends can repair a dilapidated tractor. His Newfoundland dog shares his concern. This was made for Doc's birthday to help raise funds for his boys' camp."

SML 381 Johnny Appleseed, Patron Saint of the Apple Industry (Commercial) *1967/2,000*

"This figurine was made for one of the leading applesauce processors who used it as an advertising piece."

SML 382 Johnny Appleseed *1967/Open (6203)*

"Same as above, but used in the retail line."

SML 383 Uncle Sam *1967/Open (6206)*

"He was really Sam Wilson, a cousin of John Chapman who was Johnny Appleseed. Both lived, at one time, in Mason, NH. This figure was originally made for the observance of a celebration in that town. It was later put in the retail line."

SML 384 The Colonial Watchman *1967/Open (6208)*

"This is a figure in colonial costume holding a large lantern to light the citizens' home."

SML 385 Ortho-Novum *1967/500*

"This shows a doctor standing in front of his file cabinets and ordering a snake who has slipped down from his position on the caduceus (The Twin Serpents of Hermes)."

SML 386 Nurse *1967/Open (6212)*

Originally made for Mead-Johnson and then put into the retail line."

SML 387 Robert E. Lee *1967/Open (6009)*

"The General and his horse, Traveler. This horse went through the entire Civil War with General Lee."

SML 388 Concord Minuteman *1967/Open (6250)*

"This is from the statue by Daniel Chester French in Concord, Massachusetts."

SML 389 Lexington Minuteman *1968/SSR*

"From the H. H. Kitson statue of Captain John Parker in Lexington, Massachusetts."

SML 390 Drummer Boy *1968/Open (6209)*

"A boy in Revolutionary costume with a red drum."

SML 391 Colonial Blacksmith *1968/Open (6219)*

"A man in colonial costume working at an anvil."

SML 392 Old Mill Plaque *1968/Prototype*

"Made for a chocolate manufacturer who cast the design in chocolate."

SML 393 Mayflower *1970/300*

"Made exclusively for The New Jersey Society of Mayflower descendants."

SML 394 Uncle Sam in Orbit *1970/SSR*

"After the success of the astronauts, Uncle Sam was placed in front of the Earth, holding the Moon on his shoulder."

SML 395 Home from the Sea *1970/Open (6327)*

"A sailor just returning from a voyage is met by his girlfriend."

SML 396 Ye Chairman Takes Ye Floor (Plaque)
1971/SSR

"This was made as a presentation piece for people serving at New England Town Meetings. The figure is frantically waving documents to substantiate his oratorical efforts."

SML 397 Colonial Overseer *1972/Open (6259)*

"Since Jordan Marsh was finished with their promotions, we adapted the design for the retail line."

SML 398 George and the Hatchet *1972/SSR*

"A stylized version of Washington for the retail line."

SML 399 Martha and the Cherry Pie *1972/SSR*

"A companion for George and the Hatchet."

SML 400 Sidewalk Days (Boy) *1978/ Limited to 10,000*

SML 401 Sidewalk Days (Girl)

"I designed this pair in 1938 but never sold them. Using the old molds, we issued this as a limited edition of 10,000 and the complete edition was sold."

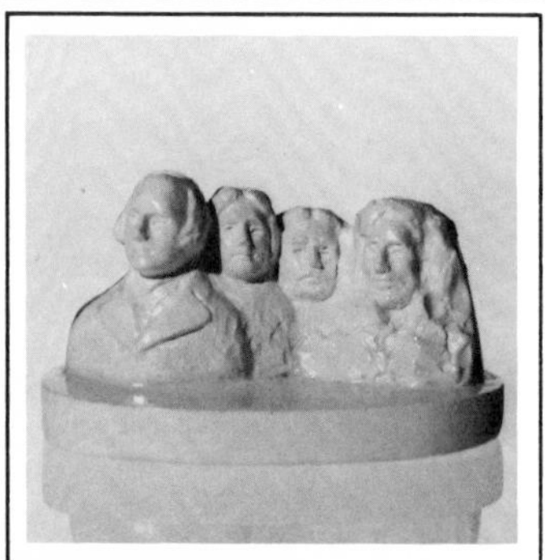

SML 402 Mt. Rushmore *1978/ Open (6010)*

"A miniature version of Gutzon Borglum's National Memorial at Mt. Rushmore, South Dakota."

SML 403 Family Sing (America Remembers)
1978/ Open
(6601)
(Discontinued forever Dec. 31, 1979)

"A family group is gathered about a Victorian square piano for a sing. A paisley shawl is draped over one end and the family stands at the other side."

SML 404 Rub a Dub Dub, Three Men In a Tub
1978/ Open
(6404)

"These boys are very active in restraining the butcher's goose who wants to eat the baker's cake. The candlestick maker is trying to protect his candle."

SML 405 Skipping Rope *1978/Open (6237)*

"Another girl from Godey's Ladies Book *(SML 220-225) who is about to skip down the street."*

SML 406 Little Sister *1979/Open (6238)*

"This is also from Godey's Ladies Book *and shows a young boy reassuring his shy little sister."*

SML 407 Building Days (Girl) *1979/(6261) Limited to 10,000*

"A girl has built a tower of blocks to nearly her own height. Very soon she will add the one piece that will cause the whole pile to collapse."

SML 408 Building Days (Boy) *1979/(6260) Limited to 10,000*

"A boy is building a garage of blocks for his red steam shovel."

SML 409 Family Picnic (America Remembers)

1979/(6602)

To be discontinued forever on Dec. 31, 1980

"The same family of four in Family Sing (SML 403). They are having a leisurely lunch in the park."

SML 410 Snow Days (Girl) *1979/(6263)*

Limited to 10,000

"A young miss puts the finishing touches on her snowman."

SML 411 Snow Days (Boy) *1979/(6262)*

Limited to 10,000

"This young fellow prepares his fort well in anticipation of the snowball battle to come."

INDEX

	SML No.
Snow Days (Girl)	410
Songs at Cratchits	47
Mrs. S.O.S.	322
Speak For It	225
Speedy Alka-Seltzer	283
Spirit of '76	102
Spirit of '76 (Paperweight)	147
Stagecoach	331
Stagecoach (Pen Stand)	330
R. H. Stearns Couple	57
Stork (Jello)	218
Annie Stuyvesant	24
Peter Stuyvesant	23
Peter Stuyvesant	334
Supp-hose Lady	339
Supp-hose Lady (Pen Stand)	340
The Swan Boat	161
Swan Boat (Empty Seats—Brooch)	253
Swan Boat (Full Seats—Brooch)	254
Swedish Boy	107
Swedish Girl	106
Switching the Freight	222
Sylvania Display Stand	281
Tabasco Sauce	204
Texcel Tape (Johnson & Johnson)	269
Becky Thatcher	108
Judge Thatcher	89
The Thinker	131
The Thinker (Pen Stand)	132
Three Little Kittens (Jello)	268
Eustace Tilly, Esq.	137

	SML No.
Toll House Town Crier (Pen Stand)	71
Toll House Town Crier	70
Touchstone, the Jester	156
The Town Crier	159
The Tower of Tape (Permacel)	270
Aunt Betsy Trotwood	45
Tuba	37
Mark Twain	335
Mark Twain's Home	133
Oliver Twist and the Parish Beadle	115
Katrina Von Tassel	141
Dame Van Winkle	144
Rip Van Winkle	145
Giovanni Verazzano	326
Victorian Couple	297
George Washington	3
George Washington and Cannon	66
George Washington, Mason	351
George and Martha Washington	300
Martha Washington	4
The Weaver	187
Weaver (Alexander Smith)	324
Weighing the Baby	211
Sam Weller	44
Whale (Jello)	236
Williamsburg Couple	299
Williamsburg Governor	7
Williamsburg Lady	8
Wisemen	349
Yankee Clipper Ship	245
Yankee Sea Captain	130